OLD JUNK

Books by

H . M . T O M L I N S O N

THE SEA AND THE JUNGLE

OLD JUNK

LONDON RIVER

WAITING FOR DAYLIGHT

OLD JUNK

By H. M. TOMLINSON

FOREWORD BY S. K. RATCLIFFE

NEW YORK   ALFRED · A · KNOPF   1923

PRINTED IN THE UNITED STATES OF AMERICA

To

C. H. G. H.

Who saw with me so much of
what is in this book

(Killed in action in Artois, August 27th, 1918)

THESE stories of travel and chance have been selected from writings published in various periodicals between January 1907 and April 1918, and are arranged in order of time.

Foreword

The author of Old Junk *has been called a legend. A colleague who during the later stages of the war visited the western front assured me that this was the right word by which to describe the memory left among officers and men, not so much by his work as a war correspondent, as by his original and fascinating character. A legend, too, he appears to be in the newspaper world of London: but there in a different sense, by reason of the singular contradiction between the human creature beloved of all his fellows and the remarkable productions of his pen.*

The first thing to say about H. M. Tomlinson, the thing of which you become acutely aware on making his acquaintance, is that he is a Londoner. "Nearly a pure-blooded London Saxon" is his characterization of himself. And so it is. He could have sprung from no other stock. In person and speech, in the indefinable quality of the man, in the humour which continually tempers his tremendous seriousness, he belongs to London. Among the men of our time who have done cre-

Foreword

ative writing I can think of no other about whom
this can be so precisely stated.

It was in the opening years of the century that I
first began to notice his work. His name was ap-
pearing in the columns of a London morning newspaper, since absorbed by the Daily News, over articles which, if my memory is not at fault, were
mainly concerned with the life of Thames side.
They were written with extraordinary care. The
man who did them had, clearly, no competitor in
Fleet Street. And he furnishes a striking illustra-
tion of the chances and misfits of the journalistic
life. When, after some years of absence in the
Far East, I was able to fit a person to the writing
which had so long attracted me, I found H. M.
Tomlinson on the regular reporting staff of a great
London newspaper. A man born for the creation
of beauty in words was doing daily turn along
with the humble chronicler of metropolitan trivi-
alities.

A year or two before the war the quality of his
mind and of his style was revealed in THE SEA
AND THE JUNGLE — a "narrative of the voyage
of the tramp steamer Capella, from Swansea to
Para in the Brazils, and thence two thousand miles
along the forests of the Amazon and Madeira
Rivers to the San Antonio Falls," returning by

Foreword

Barbados, Jamaica, and Tampa. Its author called it merely "an honest book of travel." It is that no doubt; but in a degree so eminent, one is tempted to say that an honest book of travel, when so conceived and executed, must surely count among the noblest works of the literary artist.

The great war provided almost unlimited work for men of letters, and not seldom work that was almost as far from their ordinary business as fighting itself. It carried Tomlinson into the guild of war correspondents. In the early months he represented the paper to which for some years he had been attached, the London Daily News. *Later, under the co-operative scheme which emerged from the restrictive policy adopted by all the belligerent governments, his dispatches came to be shared among a partnership which included the London* Times — *as odd an arrangement for a man like Tomlinson as could well be imagined. It would be foolish to attempt an estimate of his correspondence from France. It was beautiful copy, but it was not war reporting. To those of us who knew him it remained a marvel how he could do it at all. But there was no marvel in the fact, attested by a notable variety of witnesses, of Tomlinson as an influence and a memory, persisting until the dispersal of the armies, as of one who*

[13]

Foreword

was the friend of all, a sweet and fine spirit moving untouched amid the ruin and terror, expressing itself everywhere with perfect simplicity, and at times with a shattering candor.

From France he returned, midway in the war, to join the men who, under the Command of H. W. Massingham, make the editorial staff of the London Nation *the most brilliant company of journalists in the world. His hand may be traced week by week in many columns and especially, in alternate issues, on the page given up to the literary* causerie.

To the readers of books Tomlinson is known at present by THE SEA AND THE JUNGLE *alone. The war, it may be, did something to retard its fame. But the time is coming when none will dispute its right to a place of exceptional honour among records of travel — alongside the very few which, during the two or three decades preceding the general overturn, had been added to the books of the great wayfaring companions. It is remarkably unlike all others, in its union of accurate chronicle with intimate self-revelation; and, although it is the sustained expression of a mood, it is extremely quotable. I choose as a single example this scene, from the description of the* Capella's *first day on the Para River.*

[14]

Foreword

*There was seldom a sign of life but the infrequent
snowy herons, and those curious brown fowl, the ciganas.
The sun was flaming on the majestic assembly of the storm.
The warm air, broken by our steamer, coiled over us in a
lazy flux. . . . Sometimes we passed single habitations on
the water side. Ephemeral huts of palm-leaves were
forced down by the forest, which overhung them, to wade
on frail stilts. A canoe would be tied to a toy jetty, and
on the jetty a sad woman and several naked children would
stand, with no show of emotion, to watch us go by. Behind them was the impenetrable foliage. I thought of the
precarious tenure on earth of these brown folk with some
sadness, especially as the day was going. The easy domi-
nance of the wilderness, and man's intelligent morsel of
life resisting it, was made plain when we came suddenly
upon one of his little shacks secreted among the aqueous
roots of a great tree, cowering, as it were, between two of
the giant's toes. Those brown babies on the jetties never
cheered us. They watched us, serious and forlorn.
Alongside their primitive huts were a few rubber trees,
which we knew by their scars. Late in the afternoon we
came to a large cavern in the base of the forest, a shadowy
place where at last we did see a gathering of the folk. A
number of little wooden crosses peeped above the floor in
the hollow. The sundering floods and the forest do not
always keep these folk from congregation, and the comfort
of the last communion.*

*If the reader is also a writer, he will feel the
challenge of that passage — its spiritual quality,
its rhythm, its images. And he will know what*

[15]

Foreword

gifts of mind, and what toil, have gone to its making.

OLD JUNK *is not, in the same organic sense, a book. The sketches and essays of which it is composed are of different years and, as a glance will show, of a wide diversity of theme. The lover of the great book will be at home with the perfect picture of the dunes, as well as with the two brilliantly contrasted voyages; while none who can feel the touch of the interpreter will miss the beauty of the pieces that may be less highly wrought.*

As to Tomlinson's future I would not venture a prediction. Conceivably, when the horror has become a memory that can be lived with and transfused, he may write one of the living books enshrining the experience of these last five years. But, just as likely he may not. I subscribe, in ending this rough note, to a judgment recently delivered by a fellow worker that among all the men writing in England today there is none known to us whose work reveals a more indubitable sense of the harmonies of imaginative prose.

S. K. RATCLIFFE.

New York, Christmas, 1919.

[16]

CONTENTS

OLD JUNK

I. The African Coast

I

SHE is the steamship *Celestine*, and she is but a little lady. The barometer has fallen, and the wind has risen to hunt the rain. I do not know where *Celestine* is going, and, what is better, do not care. This is December and this is Algiers, and I am tired of white glare and dust. The trees have slept all day. They have hardly turned a leaf. All day the sky was without a flaw, and the summer silence outside the town, where the dry road goes between hedges of arid prickly pears, was not reticence but vacuity. But I sail tonight, and so the barometer is falling, and I do not know where *Celestine* will take me. I do not care where I go with one whose godparents looked at her and called her that.

There is one place called Jidjelli we shall see, and there is another called Collo; and there are many others, whose names I shall never learn, tucked away in the folds of the North African hills where they come down to the sea between Algiers and Carthage. They will reveal themselves as I find my way to Tripoli of Barbary. I am bound for Tripoli, without any reason except that I like the name and admire *Celestine*, who is going part of the journey.

But the barometer, wherever I am, seems to know when I embark. It falls. When I went aboard the wind was howling through the shipping in the harbour of Algiers. And again, *Celestine* is French, and so we can do little more than smile at each other to make visible the friendship of our two great nations. A cable is clanking slowly, and sailors run and shout in great excitement, doing things I can see no reason for, because it is as dark and stormy as the forty days.

Algiers is a formless cluster of lower stars, and presently those stars begin to revolve about us as though the wind really had got the sky loose. The *Celestine* is turning her head for the sea. The stars then speed by our masts and funnel till the last is gone. Good-bye, Algiers!

Celestine begins to curtsy, and at last becomes somewhat hysterical. At night, in a high wind, she seems but a poor little body to be out alone, with me. Tripoli becomes more remote than I thought it to be in the early afternoon, when the

The African Coast

French sailor talked to me in a café while he drank something so innocently pink that it could not account altogether for his vivacity and sudden open friendship for a shy alien. He wanted me to elope with *Celestine*. He wanted to show me his African shore, to see his true Mediterranean. I had travelled from Morocco to Algiers, and was tired of tourist trains, historic ruins, hotels, Arabs selling picture-postcards and worse, and girls dancing the dance of the Ouled-Nails to the privileged who had paid a few francs to see them do it. I had observed that tranquil sea; and in places, as at Oran, had seen in the distance terraces of coloured rock poised in enchantment between a blue ceiling and a floor of malachite.

That sea is now on our port beam. It goes before an inshore gale, and lifts us high, turns us giddy with a sudden betrayal and descent; and does it again, and again. Africa has vanished. Where Algiers probably was there are but several frail stars far away in the dark that soar in a hurry, and then collapse into the deep and are doused.

But here is le Capitaine. There is no need, of course, to be anxious for *Celestine*. If her master is not a sailor, then all the signs are wrong. He looks at me roguishly. Ah! His ship rolls.

[23]

Old Junk

But the mistake, it is not his. What would I have? She was built in England. *Voilà!*

He is a little dark man, with quick, questioning eyes, and hair like a clothesbrush. His short alert hair, his raised and querulous eyebrows, his taut moustaches, and a bit of beard that hangs like a dagger from his under lip, give him the appearance of constant surprise and fretfulness. When he is talking to me he is embarrassingly playful — but I shall show him presently, with fair luck, that my inelastic Saxon putty can transmute itself, can also volatilise in abandonment to sparkling nonsense; yet not tonight — not tonight, monsieur. He is so gay and friendly to me whenever he sees me. But when one of the staff does that which is not down in the book, I become alarmed. Monsieur bangs the table till the cruet-stoppers leap out, and his eyes are unpleasant. Yes, he is the master. He rises, and shakes his forefinger at the unfortunate till his hand is a quivering haze and his speech a blast. " Ou — é — e — eh! " cries the skipper at last, when the unfortunate is on the run.

He has an idea I cannot read the menu, so when an omelette is served he informs me, in case I should suppose it is a salad. He makes helpful farmyard noises. There is no mistaking eggs.

The African Coast

There is no mistaking pork. But I think he has the wrong pantomime for the ship's beef, unless French horses have the same music as English cows. After the first dinner, I was indiscreet enough to refuse the cognac with the coffee. " Ah ! " he chided, smiling with craft, and shaking a knowing finger at me. He could read my native weakness. I was discovered. " Viskee ! You 'ave my viskee ! " A dreadful doubt seized me, and I would have refused, but repressed my panic, and pretended he had found my heart.

He rose, and shouted a peremptory order. A little private cabinet was opened. A curious bot-tle was produced, having a deadly label in red, white, and green. " Viskee ! " cried the captain in exultation. (My God !) " Aha ! " said the reader of my hidden desire, pouring out the tipple for which he imagines I am perishing in stoic Brit-ish silence. " Viskee ! " I drain off, with sim-ulated delight, my large dose of methylated spirit. Not for worlds would I undeceive the good fellow, not if this were train-oil. He laughs aloud at our secret insular weakness. He knows it. But he is our very good friend.

All is not finished with the whisky. Out comes the master's English Grammar, for he is wishful to know us better before I leave him. And he

shall. To this Frenchman I determine to be
nobler than I was made. I think I would teach
him English all the way to Cochin-China. He
writes in his notebook, very slowly, while his
tongue comes out to look on, a sentence like this:
" The nombres Française, they are most easy that
the English language." Then I put him right;
and then he rises, reaches his hands up to my
shoulders, looks earnestly in my eyes, and la-las
my National Anthem. It may please God not to
let me look so foolish as I feel while I wait for
the end of that tune; but I doubt that it does.

II

Early next morning we arrived at Bougie, to
get an hour's peace with the arm of the harbour
thrown about my poor *Celestine*. The deck of a
Grimsby trawler discharging fish in the Humber
on a wet December morning is no more desolating
than was the look of *Celestine* under the mountains of Bougie; and Bougie, if you have a
memory for the coloured posters, is in the blue
Mediterranean. But do I grumble? I do not.
With all the world but slops, cold iron, and squalls
of sleet, I prefer *Celestine* to Algiers.

Most likely you have never heard of the black
Mediterranean. It is usual to go there in winter,

and write about it with a date-palm in every
paragraph, till you have got all the health and
enjoyment there is in the satisfaction of telling
others that while they are choosing cough cures
you are under a sunshade on the coral strand.
The truth is, the Middle Sea in December can
be as ugly as the Dogger Bank. There were
some Arab deck passengers on our coaster. One
of them sat looking at a deck rivet as motionless
as a fakir, and his face had the complexion of a
half-ripe watermelon. His fellow-sufferers were
only heaps of wet and dirty linen dumped in the
lee alley-way. It was bad enough in a bunk,
where you could brace your knees against the side,
and keep moderately still till you dozed off, when
naturally you were shot out sprawling into the
lost drainage wandering on the erratic floor.
What those Arabs suffered on deck I cannot tell
you. I never went up to find out. At Bougie
they seemed to have left it all to Allah, with the
usual result. It was clear, from a glance at those
piles of rags, that the Arab is no more native to
Algeria than the Esquimaux. I was much nearer
home than the Arabs. That shining coast which
occasionally I had surprised from Oran, which
seemed afloat on the sea, was no longer a vision
of magic, the unsubstantial work of Iris, an il-

lusionary cloud of coral, amber, and amethyst. It was the bare bones of this old earth, as sombre and foreboding as any ruin of granite under the wrack of the bleak north.

As for Bougie, these African villages are built but for bright sunlight. They change to miserable and filthy ruins in the rain, their white walls blotched and scabrous, and their paths mud tracks between the styes. Their lissom and statuesque inhabitants become softened and bent, and pad dejectedly through the muck as though they were ashamed to live, but had to go on with it. The palms which look so well in sunny pictures are besoms up-ended in a drizzle. They have not that equality with the storm which makes the Sussex beech and oak, heavily based and strong-armed, stand with a look of might and roar at the charges of the Channel gale. By this you will see that Bougie must wait until I call that way again. From the look of the sky, too, there is no doubt we are in for a spell of the kind of weather I never expected to meet in Africa. I was a stranger there, but I knew the language of those squadrons of dark clouds driving into the bay.

The northern sky was full of their gloomy keels. There were intervals when the full expanse of Bougie Bay became visible, with its con-

course of mountains crowded to the shore. At the
base of the dark declivities the combers were
bursting, and the spume towered on the gale like
grey smoke. Out of the foam rose harsh rubble
and screes to incline against broken precipices,
and those stark walls were interrupted by mid-air
slopes of grass which appeared ready to avalanche
into the tumult below, but remained, livid areas
of a dim mass which rose into dizzy pinnacles
and domes, increasing the tumbling menace of the
sky. A fleet of clouds of deep draught ran into
Africa from the north; went aground on those
crags, were wrecked and burst, their contents
streaming from them and hiding the aerial reef
on which they had struck. The land vanished,
till only Bougie and its quay and the *Celestine*
remained, with one last detached fragment of
mountain high over us. That, too, dissolved.
There was only our steamer and the quay at last.

I thought our master would not dare to put out
from there, but he cared as little for the storm
as for the steward. His last bales were no
sooner in the lighters than he made for Jidjelli.
But Jidjelli daunted even him. The nearer
we got, the worse it looked. My own feeling was that the gathering seas had taken
charge of our scallop, a cork in the surf,

and were pitching her, helpless, towards terrible walls built of night out of a base of thunder and bursting waters. I gripped a rail, and saw a vague range of summits appear above the nearing walls and steadily develop towards distinction. Then the howling gale began to scream, the ceiling lowered and darkened, and merged with the rocks, reducing the world but to our *Celestine* in the midst of near flashes of white in an uproar. When presently a little daylight came into chaos to give it shape again, there was an inch of hail on our deck, and the mountains had been changed to white marble. We saw a red light burn low in the place where Jidjelli ought to be, a signal that it was impossible to enter. Our skipper put about.

That is all I know of Jidjelli, and all I wanted to know on such an evening. The sound of the surf on the rocks was better to hear when it was not so close. We followed that coast all night while I lay awake, shaking to the racing of the propeller; and I blessed the unknown engineers of the North Country who took forethought of nights of that kind when doing their best for *Celestine;* for, though bruised, I still loved her above Algiers and Timgad. She had character, she had set her course, and she was holding stead-

ily to it, and did not pray the uncompassionate
to change its face.

III

For more than a week we washed about in the
surf of a high, dark coast towards Tunis. We
might have been on the windward side of Ultima
Thule. Supposing you could have been taken
miraculously from your fogs and midday lamps of
London, and put with me in the *Celestine,* and
told that that sullen land looming through the
murk could be yours, if you could guess its name,
then you would have guessed nothing below the
fortieth parallel.

No matter; when you were told, you would
have laughed at your loss. Now you understood
why it was called the Dark Continent. It looked
the home of slavery, murder, rhinoceroses, the
Congo, war, human sacrifices, and gorillas. It
had the forefront of the world of skulls and hor-
rors, ultimatums, mining concessions, chains, and
development. Its rulers would be throned on
bone-heaps. You will say (of course you will
say) that I saw Africa like that because I was
weary of the place. Not at all. I was merely
looking at it. The feeling had been growing on
me since first I saw Africa at Oran, where I

[31]

landed   The longer I stay, the more depressed I get.

This has nothing to do with the storm. This African shadow does not chill you because you wish you were home, and home is far away. It does not come of your rare and lucky idleness, in which you have to do nothing but enjoy yourself; generally a sufficient reason for melancholy, though rarely so in my own case. No, Africa itself is the reason. There is an invisible emanation from its soil, the aura of evil in antiquity. You cannot see it, at first you are unaware it is there, and cannot know, therefore, what is the matter with you. This haunting premonition is different from mere wearying and boredom. It gets worse, the longer you stay; it goes deeper than sadness, it descends into a conviction of something that is without hope, that is bad in its nature, and unrepentant in its arrogant heart. When you have got so far down you have had time to discover what that is which has put you so low. The day may be radiant, the sky just what you had hoped to find in Africa, and the people in the market-place a lively and chromatic jangle; but the shadow of what we call inhumanity (when we are trying to persuade ourselves that humanity is something very different) chills and darkens the heart.

Yet the common sky of North Africa might be the heaven of the first morning, innocent of knowledge that night is to come. It is not a hard blue roof; your sight is lost in the atmosphere which is azure. The sun more than shines; his beams ring on the rocks, and glance in colours from the hills. From a distance the flowers on a hill slope will pour down to the sea in such a torrent of hues that you might think the arch of the rainbow you saw there had collapsed in the sun and was now rills and cascades. The grove of palms holding their plumes above a white village might be delicate pencillings on the yellow sheet of desert. The heat is a balm. The shadows are stains of indigo on the roads and pale walls.

IV

One day we found Sfax. I went ashore at Sfax, interested in a name quite new to me. The guide-book did not even mention it; perhaps it was not worth while; no ruins, mummies, trams or hotels there, of course. Maybe it was only the name of a man, or a grass, or a sort of phosphate. Sfax! Well, anyhow, I had long wished for

Old Junk

Africa, anywhere in Africa, and here I was, not eager to get home again, but not disinclined. What I had seen of it so far was a rather too frequented highway opposite the coast of Europe — a complementary establishment. Progress had macadamised it. Commerce and its wars had graded and uniformed and drilled its life. Its silent people marched in ranks, as it were, along mapped roads foredoomed, and its mills went round. Its life was expressed for export. It was on the way to Manchester and success. Of all the infernal uses to which a country can be put there is none like development. Let every good savage make incantation against it, or, if to some extent he has been developed, cross himself against the fructification of the evil. As for us whites, we are eternally damned, for we cannot escape the consequences of our past cleverness. The Devil has us on a complexity of strings, and some day will pull the whole lot tight. But Sfax! Had I escaped? Was there a chance?

I found a city wall, a huge battlement, ancient and weathered, like an unscalable cliff, and going through its gate was entering the shadows of a cave. Out of the glare of the sun I went into the gloom of deep, narrow, and mysterious passages. The sun was only on the parapets and casements,

which leaned towards each other confidentially,
and left only a ragged line of light above. These
alley-ways were crowded with camels, asses, and
strange men. An understanding and sneering
camel in a narrow passage will force you to take
what chance there is of escape in desecrating a
mosque, while Moslems watch you as the only
Christian there, or of going under its slobber-
ing mouth and splay feet. It does not care
which.

It was market-day for Sfax. There were little
piles of vivid fruit beside white walls where a
broad ray of sunlight found them. There were
silversmiths at work, tent-makers, and the makers
of camel harness. The tanners had laid skins
for us to walk over. There were exotic smells.
I went exploring the crooked turnings with an indifference which was studied. I was getting an
interesting time, but was distinctly conscious of
eyes, a ceaseless stream of eyes that floated by,
watchful though making no sign. Several times
I found myself jostled with some roughness. It
occurred to me that I had heard on the ship that
Sfax was the only town which had offered resistance to the French; its men have a fine reputa-
tion throughout Tunisia, which they do something now and then to maintain, in consequence.

Old Junk

They certainly appeared a sturdy and virile lot.
They were not listless, like the Arabs of Algeria,
who have nothing to show for themselves but the
haughty and aloof bearing of the proud but beaten.

Having discovered that the enemy was vulnerable though strong, the men of Sfax go through
the day now with the directed activity of those
who once had got the worst of it, but have a
hope of doing better next time. They gave me
a lively and adventurous scene. They moved
with silent and stealthy quickness. Their eyes
glanced sideways from under their cowls. Their
hands were hidden under their jibbahs. A few
of them stared with the hate of the bereft. It
is not possible to face everybody in a press which
moves in all directions, and I was the only Euro-
pean who was there.

Passing a mosque, where I noticed the Moslems
had attempted, but had not completed, the ob-
literation of some representations of birds,— so
the mosque was once, evidently, a place where
other gods had been worshipped,— I hesitated,
wishing to look closer into this curiosity, but recol-
lected myself, and was passing on. An Arab in
the turban of one who had been to Mecca was
squatting cross-legged on the old marble pavement outside the mosque, and I just took in that

[36]

he was a fine venerable fellow with an important
beard, with a look of wisdom and experience in
his steady glance from under the strong arches
of his eyebrows that made me wish I knew Arabic,
and could squat beside him, and gossip of the wide
world. As I turned he said quietly, " Good
day ! "

Now I thought perhaps I was bewitched, but
turned and looked at him. " How are you? "
he asked. At that moment, when his eyes looking upward had a smile of understanding mischief,
and in such an alien city as Sfax, I was prepared
to declare there is but one God and Mahomet
is His prophet. For that sort of thing comes
easy to me; and would have been quite true, as
far as it went. Then I went back to him, and
fearing that after all I might be addressing but
the parrot which had already exhausted its vocab-
ulary, I tried it on him: " Shall I take my boots
off here, father, or may I sit down with you? "

" Sit down," he said.

He was a man of medicine. He sold there
prophylactics against small-pox, adultery, blind-
ness, the evil eye, sterility, or any other trouble
which you thought threatened you. If a man
feared for the faithfulness of his spouse, it seems
Father the Hadj could secure it with a charm,

and so allow him to spend the night elsewhere in perfect enjoyment and content. That is what the quiet old cynic told me, and invited me to inspect his display of amulets and fetishes, coloured glass tablets with Arabic inscriptions, and a deal of stuff which looked unreasonable to me, articles the holy man either could not or would not resolve into sense.

His English, which he had learned as a shipping agent for the pilgrim traffic, soon reached its narrow limits, to my sorrow. When it left common objects and we wished to compare our world (for there is no doubt he was an experienced and understanding elder who knew to within a little what he might expect of his God and of his fellows), we were left smiling at each other, and had to guess the rest. Yet at least the bazaar could witness this good Moslem of age and admitted wisdom sitting opposite a dubious Christian in a companionable manner; and there was that testimony to my advantage. They even watched him draw his finger across his throat in serious and energetic pantomime, and saw me nod in grave appreciation, when he was trying to make me understand what was his sympathy for the Christian conquerors of Sfax.

I went outside the landward gate of the city,

The African Coast

and looked out over the level of brilliant sand
which stretched out from there to Lake Tchad.
What a voyage! What a lure! Perhaps there
is no more perilous journey on earth than that,
and if a traveller would vanish into the past, into
such Oriental countries as the voyagers of Hakluyt
saw with wonder, then to leave Sfax, and go across
country to the Niger, would equal what once came
of fooling with the arcana of the Djinn. Though,
after all, one would like to emerge again, to tell
the tale to the children; and the whole dubiety
of it is in that last difficulty. It is almost certain
the magic would be too powerful.

About the bright yellow sea of the desert which
came up to the high cliffs of the town, the squatting camels made dark hummocks. Strings of
donkeys converged on the city gate bearing water-
pots and baskets of charcoal. Sometimes a line
of camels swayed outwards through the crowd,
disappeared among the shrines, going south.
Watching such a caravan go was the same as
watching a ship leave port.

By the wayside was a huckster. He banged
a tomtom till he had gathered a crowd from the
loose concourse of men who had come long jour-
neys with esparto grass, or gums and ostrich
plumes, and much else from the secret region in-

[39]

land. He was selling cotton shirts, and was an
entertaining villain. By the corners of his mouth
his humour was leery. He did not laugh, but
his grimaces were funny. The variegated crowd
and that huckster was too enticing, and forgetting
I had not seen one of my own kind since leaving
the ship, and that my face among those black and
brown masks was as loud as the tomtom, I mingled
my outrageous tourist tweeds with the graceful
folds of the robes. The huckster kept glancing
at me, and from grave side-long glances that crowd
of men went to the extraordinary length of grim
smiles. Suddenly I recognized the trick of that
Arab cheapjack. It may be seen at work in Poplar, my native parish to which the ships come,
when a curious and innocent Chinaman joins the
group about the fluent quack i the market place.

As soon as dignity permitt I passed on, and
my dignity did not keep me waiting for any length
of time.

Uncertain, and not a little nervous, I wandered
among some plantations of olives and false pep-
pers, where the domes of the tombs floated like
white bubbles on the foliage. Here an Arab
beckoned to me, and told me he had been watching me for some time — for he was an English
medical missionary in disguise — and warned me

that these gardens and shrines were quite the
wrong place to wander in alone. It appears that
only a few days since the flame of insurrection
flashed down the bazaar, licked up a few French
soldiers who happened to be there, and had almost got a hold before the garrison appeared and
doused it. He took me to his house, with its
windows heavily barred, for there his predeces-
sor had been murdered. (If this could happen
at the starting-place for Lake Tchad, then let the
idea go.)

From the flat roof of the doctor's house I
smelt the dung of ages, fought with legions of
flies, and looked down on a large quadrangle of
hay and stable muck, where camels had carefully
folded themselves on the ground, and chewed re-
flectively, their eyes half closed; and large drowsy
asses mechanically fanned their ears at the loathly
swarms. The missionary surmised that the car-
avanserai below was the perfect reflection of one
we had heard more about, which was once at
Bethlehem. The square was enclosed with flat-
roofed stables, and it being a busy time they were
all occupied. The first one, immediately below
us, was filled with a family of Kabyles, which con-
sisted chiefly of a magnificent virago of a wife,
tattooed, with a fine gold ring in her nostrils,

who seemed to have a trying life with her mild
and contemplative old husband. She had more
children than one could count without giving the
matter that close attention which might be misin-
terpreted. She cradled them in the manger
every night. Loud as her voice was, though, I
could almost hear the old man smile as he walked
away from her. They had two contemptuous
camels who never lifted an eyelid when she raised
her voice to them, but chewed calmly on, with
faces turned impassively towards the New Jeru-
salem of camels, where viragoes are not; and several resigned asses who appeared to have handed
their souls back to their Maker, because souls are
but extra trammels in this place of sorrow.

Next door to them was a regular tenant who
bred goats, and fed them out of British biscuit-
tins. Beyond them the stable was occupied by a
party of swarthy ruffians who had arrived with
a cargo of esparto grass. In the far corner, a
family, crowded out, had been living for weeks
under a structure of horrible rags. Smoke, issu-
ing from a dozen seams, gave their home the
look of a smouldering manure heap.

The African Coast

V

You probably know there are place-names
which, when whispered privately, have the unreasonable power of translating the spirit east
of the sun and west of the moon. They cannot
be seen in print without a thrill. The names in
the atlas which do that for me are a motley lot,
and you, who see no magic in them, but have your
own lunacy in another phase, would laugh at mine.
Celebes, Acapulco, Para, Port Royal, Cartagena,
the Marquesas, Panama, the Mackenzie River,
Tripoli of Barbary. They are some of mine.
Rome should be there, I know, and Athens, and
Byzantium. But they are not, and that is all
I can say about it.

Why give reasons for our preferences? How
often have our preferences any reason? Maybe
some old scoundrel of an ancestor who made a
fortune (all lost since) as a thief on the Spanish
main, whispers Panama to me when my mind is
tired. Others may make magic with Ostend,
Biarritz, or Ancoats; and they are just as lucky
as the man who obtains the spell by looking at
the Dry Tortugas on the map.

When I set out from Newport on this voyage,
I did not expect to see Tripoli of Barbary. We

have never considered the possibility that our
favourite place-names really do stand for stones
that have veritable shapes and smells under a sun
which comes and goes daily. Nor was my
steamer exactly the sort of craft which could,
by the look of her, ever attain to the coast of Barbary. What would a steamer know about it?
She would never fetch the landfall of a dream. I
was not surprised, therefore, when she fetched
Tripoli quite wrong; not the place at all for which
I was looking on the southern horizon. But then,
she was but taking crockery there, in crates; and
crockery is less vulnerable, is rough freight, com-
pared to a fancy. The crockery, however, got to
its Tripoli quite safely.

We anchored; and there was Tripoli, standing round a little bay, with its buildings, variously
coloured, crowded to the west, and slender min-
arets standing as masts over the flat decks of the
houses. I landed at a narrow water-gate, and
the Turkish officials regarded me as though I had
come to remove the country. When I wished to
embark again, these curious people in uniform
were even more serious than when I arrived.
After a long hesitation, permission was given me
niggardly to leave Tripoli, and my ship's boatmen
pointed out the urgent need to supply a certain

rowboat in the bay with that morsel of paper. To lose that tiny document would have a shocking result, for a warship was in the bay to support the rowboat. We passed that warship. Some day a hilarious traveller will tear his document into fragments, and that warship will fire at him, and sink. The system here, a mere tabulation of fear and suspicion, those reflexes of evildoers who have the best of reasons to be jealous of their neighbours, is protective exclusiveness in its perfect flower, and perhaps it would be better to be really dead than to live under it as a warm, lawabiding corpse.

I should guess that, with a slight magnification to make the object plainer, there are three soldiers to each worker in North Africa. On from Oran the gaudy fellow in uniform has been very conspicuous, the most leisured and prosperous of the inhabitants, and one came unwillingly to the conclusion that it is more profitable to smoke cigarettes in a country than to grow corn in it. As for Tripoli, its uniformed protectors hide the protected; but perhaps its natives have learned how to live by killing one another. It is possible I have not divined the more subtle ways of God's providence.

Tripoli, like other towns on these shores, looks

Old Junk

as though it were sloughing away. Where stones fall, there they lie. In the centre of the town is a marble triumphal arch in honour of Marcus Aurelius. Age would account for much of its ruin, but not all; yet it still stands cold, haughty, austere, though decrepit, in Tripolitan mud, with mean stucco and plaster buildings about it. The arch itself is filled in, and is used as a dwelling. Its tenant is a greengrocer, and the monument to Marcus Aurelius has an odour of garlic; but it need not be supposed that that was specially repugnant to me. How could the white marble of Marcus, to say nothing of a warmer philosophy no less austere, be acceptable to our senses unless translated, with a familiar odour of garlic, by modern greengrocers? I shall think more of Tripoli of Barbary in future, when looking back at it through a middle-aged pipe, when the chains have got me at last.

January 1907.

[46]

II. The Call

WHEN the train left me at Clayton Station, the only passenger to alight, its hurried retreat down the long straight of converging metals, a rapidly diminishing cube, seemed to be measuring for me the isolation of the place. Clayton appeared to be two railway platforms and a row of elms across an empty road. After the last rumble of the train, which had the note of a distant cry of derision, there closed in the quiet of a place where affairs had not even begun. It was raining, there was a little luggage, I did not know the distance to the village, and the porter had disappeared. A defective gutter-spout overhead was the leaking conduit for all the sounds and movement of the countryside.

Then I saw a boy humped into the shelter of a shrub which leaned over the station fence. He was reading. Before him was a hand-cart lettered " Humphrey Monk, Grocer and General Dealer, Clayton." The boy wore spectacles

[47]

Old Junk

which, when he looked at me, magnified his eyes
so that the lad seemed a luminous and disembodied stare. I saw only the projection of his
enlarged gaze. He promised to take my luggage
to Clayton. I walked through three miles of
steady rain to the village, by a stretch of marsh-
land so hushed by the nearness of the draining
sky that the land might have been what it seemed
at a little distance: merely a faint presentment
of fields solvent in the wet. Its green melted into
the outer grey at a short distance where rows of
elms were smeared. There was nothing beyond.

This old village of Clayton is five miles inland from Clayton-on-Sea, that new and popular
resort hardened with asphalt and concrete, to
which city folk retire for a change in the summer.
During the winter months many of the shops of
the big town are closed till summer brings the
holiday-makers again. The porticoes of the
abandoned premises fill with street litter, old
paper, and straws. The easterly winds cut the
life out of the streets, the long ranks of automatic
machines look out across the empty parade, and
rust, and the lines of the pier-deck advance deso-
lately far into the wind and grey sea, straight and
uninterrupted. It is more than barren then,
Clayton-on-Sea, for man has been there, builded

The Call

busily and even ornately, loaded the town with
structures for even his minor whims in idleness;
and forsaken it all. So it will look on the Last
Day. The advertisements clamour pills and hair-
dye to a town which seems as if the Judgment Day
has passed and left the husk of life. So I was
driven to the original Clayton, the place which
gave the name, the little inland village that did,
when I found it, show some signs of welcome life.
It was a clump of white cottages in a vague cloud
of trees. It had some chimneys smoking, there
was a man several fields away, and a dog sitting
in a porch barked at me. Here was a little of
the warmth of human contiguity.

When night came, and the village was but a
few chance and unrelated lights, there was the
choice between my bedroom and the taproom of
the inn where I lodged. In the bedroom, crown-
ing a chest of drawers, was a large Bible, and on
the wall just above was a glass case of shabby sea-
birds, their eyes so placed that they appeared to
be looking up from Holy Writ with a look of
such fatuous rapture that one's idea of immor-
tality became associated with bodies dusty, stuffed,
and wired. (Oh, the wind and the rain!) Yet
there was left the bar-parlour; and there, usually,
was a dim lamp showing but a table with assorted

empty mugs, a bar with bottles and a mirror, but
nobody to serve, and a picture of Queen Victoria
in her coronation robes.

There was but one other light in Clayton which
showed sanctuary after dark for the stranger.
It was in Mr. Monk's shop. His shop at least
had its strange interests in its revelation of the
diverse needs of civilized homes, for Mr. Monk
sold everything likely to be wanted urgently
enough by his neighbours to make a journey to
greater Clayton prohibitive. In one corner of
his shop a young lady was caged, for it was also
the post office. The interior of the store was
confused with boxes, barrels, bags, and barri-
cades of smaller tins and jars, with alleys for side-
long progress between them. I do not think any
order ever embarrassed Mr. Monk. Without
hesitation he would turn, sure of his intricate
world, from babies' dummies to kerosene. There
were cards hanging from the rafters bearing briar
pipes, bottles of lotion for the hair of school-
children, samples of sauce, and stationery.

His shop had its own native smell. It was
of coffee, spices, rock-oil, cheese, bundles of wood,
biscuits, and jute bags, and yet was none of these
things, for their separate flavours were so blended
by old association that they made one indivisible

The Call

smell, peculiar, but not unpleasant, when you were used to it. I found Mr. Monk's barrel of soda quite a cherishable seat on a dull night, for the grocer's lamp was then the centre of a very dark world. Around it and beyond was only the blackness and silence of vacuity. And the grocer himself, if not busy, would give me his casual and valuable advice on the minor frailties of the human, and they seemed as engaging and confusing in their directness as a child's; for Mr. Monk was large and bland, with a pale, puffy, and unsmiling face, and only betrayed his irony with a slow wink when he was sure you were not deceived. He knew much about the gentry around, those bored and weary youths in check coats, riding breeches, and large pipes, and the young ladies in pale homespun costumes who had rude and familiar words to all they judged were their equals, and were accompanied invariably by Aberdeen terriers.

One evening I spoke to Mr. Monk of his boy. The boy, I said, seemed a strange little fellow. Mr. Monk, in his soiled, white apron, turned on me, and said nothing at first, but tapped his bald head solemnly. " Can't make him out," he said. " I think this is where it is " — and pressed a fat thumb against his head again. " But you have to

[51]

put up with any boy you can get here." He
sighed. "The bright kids go. Clear out.
There's nothing fer 'em here but farm labour an'
the poor rate. I don't know how the farmers
about here could make a do of it if we didn't pay
rates to keep their labourers from dying off. My
boys get fed up. Off they go, 'nd I doan' blame
'em. One of 'em's in a racin' stable now, doin'
well. Another's got a potman's job London
somewhere. Doin' well. But the kid I've got
now, he'll stop. No ginger in that boy. Can't
see anything five minutes off, either. Must be
under his nose, and your finger shouting at it.
He's got a cloudy mind. Yet he's clever, in his
way. There's the door-mat of the shop. As
soon as any one puts a foot on that mat, the clock
in my kitchen strikes two. All his fake. But
he does rile the customers. Silly young fool.
If there's two parcels to deliver, it's the wrong
one gets first chance."

In a land where discovery had not gone beyond
the blacksmith's forge and the arable fields, a native boy who had turned a door-mat into a watch-
dog was an interesting possibility. There the
boy was at that moment, stepping off his responsive mat, ill-clad, the red nose of his meagre face
almost as evident as his magnified stare of sur-

prised inquiry, and his mouth open. Mr. Monk
chaffed him. I spoke with some seriousness to
him, but he was shy, and gave no answer except
some throat noises. Yet presently he ceased to
rub a boot up and down one leg, and became ar-
ticulate. He mumbled that he knew the telegraph instrument too. (" Oho! " said Mr.
Monk, looking interested. " You do, do yer?
What about learning not to leave Mrs. Brown's
parcel at Mrs. Pipkin's? ") Had I ever been to
London, the boy asked, his big eyes full on my
face. Had I ever seen a Marconi station? I
talked to him, perhaps unwisely, of some of the
greater affairs. He said nothing. His mouth
remained open and his stare full-orbed.

There was one grey, still Sunday when it was
not raining, the grey sky being exhausted, and I
met the grocer's boy a little distance from the
village, sitting on a fence, reading. The boy
closed his book when he saw me, but not before
I had noticed that the volume was open at a
page showing one of those highly technical diagrams of involved machinery which only the elect
may read. I took the book — it was a manual
of civil engineering — and asked questions with
some humility; for before the man who understands the manipulating of metals and can make

Old Junk

living servants for himself out of pipes, wheels,
and valves, I stand as would a primitive or an innocent and confiding girl before the magician
who interprets for them oracles. With the confidence of long familiarity and the faint hauteur
of shyness he explained some of the diagrams in
which, at that moment, he was interested.

We talked of them, and of Clayton; for I
wished to know how this grocer's boy, who went
about masked with a mouth open a little fatuously,
an insignificant face, goggles, and a hand-truck,
himself of no account in a flat and unremarkable
place aside from the press of life's affairs, had
discovered there were hills to which he could
lift his eyes after those humiliating interviews
with Mr. Monk concerning the wrong delivery
of cheese and bacon. I was aware of the means
by which news of the outer world got to Clayton.
It came in a popular halfpenny paper, and that
outer world must therefore have seemed to Clayton to be all aeroplanes, musical-comedy girls,
dog shows, and Mr. Lloyd George. The grocer's
boy got his tongue free at last, and talked. He
was halt and obscure, but I thought I saw a mind
beating against the elms and stones of the village, and repelled by the concrete, asphalt, and
lodging-houses of the seaside place. But I am

[54]

The Call

impressionable, too. It may have been my fancy. What the boy finished with was: "There's no chance here. You never hear of anything."

You never heard of anything. That country-side really looked remote enough from the centre of affairs, from the place where men, undistracted by the news and pictures of the halfpenny illustrated Press, were getting work done. Clayton was deaf and dumb. Some miles away the smoke of the London train was streaming across the dim fields like a comet. We both stood watching that comet going sure and bright to its destiny, leaving Clayton behind, regardless of us, and as though all we there were nothing worth. We were outside the pull of life's spinning hub. Beyond and remote from us things would be happening; but no voice or pulse of life could vibrate us, merged as we were within the inelastic silence of Clayton.

We walked back to the village, and the boy said good-night, passing through a white gate to a cottage unseen at that late hour of the evening. Near midnight I left my stuffed birds, with their fixed and upturned gaze, and went into the open, where above the shapeless lumps of massive dark of Clayton the stars were detaching their arrows, for the night was clear and frosty at last. Sirius, pulsing and resplendent, seemed nearer and more vital than anything in the village.

I walked as far as the white gate of the cottage where I had left Mr. Monk's boy; and there he was again, to my surprise, at that hour. He came forward. At first he appeared to be agitated; but as he talked brokenly I saw he was exalted. He was no grocer's boy then. The lad half dragged me, finding I did not understand him, towards his home. We went round to the back of the sleeping cottage, and found a little shed. On a bench in that shed a candle was burning in a ginger-beer bottle. By the candle was a structure meaningless to me, having nothing of which I could make a guess. It was fragmentary and idle, the building which a child makes of household utensils, naming it anything to its fancy. There were old jam-pots, brass door-knobs, squares of india-rubber, an electric bell, glass rods, cotton reels, and thin wires which ran up to the roof out of sight.

"Listen!" said the grocer's boy imperatively, holding up a finger. I remained intent and suspicious, wondering. Nothing happened. I was turning to ask the lad why I should listen, for the shed was very still, and then I saw the hammer of the bell lift itself, as though alive. Some erratic and faint tinkling began. " That's my wireless," said the grocer's boy, his eyes extraordinarily bright. " I've only just finished it. Who is calling us? "

III. Old Junk

BUSINESS had brought the two of us to an inn on the West Coast, and all its windows opened on a wide harbour, hill-enclosed. Only small coasting craft were there, mostly ketches; but we had topsail schooners also and barquantines, those ascending and aerial rigs that would be flamboyant but for the transverse spars of the foremast, giving one who scans them the proper apprehension of stability and poise.

To come upon a craft rigged so, though at her moorings and with sails furled, her slender poles upspringing from the bright plane of a brimming harbour, is to me as rare and sensational a delight as the rediscovery, when idling with a book, of a favourite lyric. That when she is at anchor; but to see her, all canvas set for light summer airs, at exactly that distance where defects and harshness in her apparel dissolve, but not so far away but the white feathers at her throat are plain, is to exult in the knowledge that man once

Old Junk

reached such greatness that he imagined and created a thing which was consonant with the stateliness of the slow ranging of great billows, and the soaring density of white cumulus clouds, and with the brightness and compelling mystery of the far horizon at sundown.

Some mornings, when breakfast-time came with the top of the tide, we could look down on the plan of a deck beneath, with its appurtenances and junk, casks, houses, pumps, and winches, rope and spare spars, binnacle and wheel, perhaps a boat, the regular deck seams curving and persisting under all. An old collier ketch she might be, with a name perhaps as romantic as the *Mary Ann;* for the owners of these little vessels delight to honour their lady relatives.

Away in mid-stream the *Mary Ann* would seem but a trivial affair, no match for the immensities about her, diminished by the vistas of shores and beaches, and the hills. But seen close under our window you understood why her men would match her, and think it no hardihood, with gales and the assaults of ponderous seas. Her many timbers, so well wrought as to appear, at a distance, a delicate and frail shape, are really heavy. Even in so small a craft as a ketch they are massive enough to surprise you into wondering at the cunning of

Old Junk

shipwrights, those artists who take gross lumps of intractable timber and metal, and compel them to subtle mouldings and soft grace, to an image which we know means life that moves in rhythmic loveliness.

Talk of the art of book and picture making! There is an old fellow I met in this village who will take the ruins of a small forest, take pine boles, metal, cordage, and canvas, and without plans, but from the ideal in his eye, build you the kind of lithe and dainty schooner that, with the cadences of her sheer and moulding, and the soaring of her masts, would keep you by her side all day in harbour; build you the kind of girded, braced, and immaculate vessel, sound at every point, tuned and sweet to a precision that in a violin would make a musician flush with inspiration, a ship to ride, lissom and light, the uplifted western ocean, and to resist the violence of vaulting seas and the drive of hurricane. She will ride out of the storm afterwards, none to applaud her, over the mobile hills travelling express, the rags of her sails triumphant pennants in the gale, the beaten seas pouring from her deck.

He, that modest old man, can create such a being as that; and I have heard visitors to this village, leisured and cultured folk, whose own creative abilities amount to no more than the arranging of some decorative art in strata of merit, talk down to the old fellow who can think out a vessel like that after supper, and go out after breakfast to direct the laying of her keel — talk down to him, kindly enough, of course, and smilingly, as a " working man."

I told you there were two of us, at this inn. We met at meals. I think he was a commercial traveller. A tall young fellow, strongly built, a pleasure to look at; carefully dressed, intelligent, with hard and clear grey eyes. He had a ruddy but fastidious complexion, though he was, I noticed, a hearty and careless eater. He was energetic and swift in his movements, as though the world were easily read, and he could come to quick decisions and successful executions of his desires. He had no moments of laxity and hesitation, even after a breakfast, on a hot morning, too, of ham and eggs drenched in coffee. He made me feel an ineffective, delicate, and inferior being.

He would bang out to business, after breakfast and a breezy chat with me; and I lapsed, a lazy and shameless idler, into the window, to wonder among the models outside, the fascinating

Old Junk

curves of ships and boats, as satisfying and as personal to me as music I know, as the lilt of ballads and all that minor rhythm which wheels within the enclosing harmonies and balance of stars and suns in their orbits. Those forms of ships and boats are as satisfying as the lines which make the strength and swiftness of salmon and dolphins, and the ease of the flight of birds with great pinions; and, in a new schooner which passed this window, on her first voyage to sea — a tall and slender ship, a being so radiant in the sun as to look an evanescent and immaterial vision — as inspiring and awful as the remoteness of a spiritual and lovely woman.

" I can't make out what you see in those craft," said my companion one morning. " They're mostly ancient tubs, and at the most they only muck about the coast. Now a P. & O. or a Cunarder! That's something to look at." He was looking down at me, and there was a trace of contempt in his smile.

He was right in a way. I felt rebuked and embarrassed, and could not explain to him. These were the common objects of the Channel after all, old and weather-broken, sea wagons from the Cowes point of view, source of alarm and wonder to passengers on fine liners when they sight them

Old Junk

beating stubbornly against dirty winter weather, and hanging on to the storm. Why should they take my interest more than battleships and Cunarders? Yet I could potter about an ancient hooker or a tramp steamer all day, when I wouldn't cross a quay to a great battleship. I like the pungent smells of these old craft, just as I inhale the health and odour of fir woods. I love their men, those genuine mariners, the right diviners of sky, coast, and tides, who know exactly what their craft will do in any combination of circumstances as well as you know the pockets of your old coat; men who can handle a stiff and cranky lump of patched timbers and antique gear as artfully as others would the clever length of hollow steel with its powerful twin screws.

But when my slightly contemptuous companion spoke I had no answer, felt out of date and dull, a fogey and an idle man. I had no answer ready — none that would have satisfied this brisk young man, none that would not have seemed remote and trivial to him.

He left me. Some other visitor had left behind Stevenson's *Ebb Tide*, and trying to think out an excuse that would quiet the qualms I began to feel for this idle preference of mine for old junk, I began picking out the passages I liked.

Old Junk

And then I came on these words of Attwater's (though Stevenson, for certain, is speaking for himself): " Junk . . . only old junk! . . . Nothing so affecting as ships. The ruins of an empire would leave me frigid, when a bit of an old rail that an old shellback had leaned on in the middle watch would bring me up all standing."

IV.   Bed-Books and Night-Lights

THE rain flashed across the midnight window with a myriad feet. There was a groan in outer darkness, the voice of all nameless dreads. The nervous candle-flame shuddered by my bedside. The groaning rose to a shriek, and the little flame jumped in a panic, and nearly left its white column. Out of the corners of the room swarmed the released shadows. Black spectres danced in ecstasy over my bed. I love fresh air, but I cannot allow it to slay the shining and delicate body of my little friend the candle-flame, the comrade who ventures with me into the solitudes beyond midnight. I shut the window.

They talk of the candle-power of an electric bulb. What do they mean? It cannot have the faintest glimmer of the real power of my candle. It would be as right to express, in the same inverted and foolish comparison, the worth of "those delicate sisters, the Pleiades." That

[65]

Old Junk

pinch of star dust, the Pleiades, exquisitely remote in deepest night, in the profound where light all but fails, has not the power of a sulphur match; yet, still apprehensive to the mind though tremulous on the limit of vision, and sometimes even vanishing, it brings into distinction those distant and difficult hints — hidden far behind all our verified thoughts — which we rarely properly view. I should like to know of any great arc-lamp which could do that. So the star-like candle for me. No other light follows so intimately an author's most ghostly suggestion. We sit, the candle and I, in the midst of the shades we are conquering, and sometimes look up from the lucent page to contemplate the dark hosts of the enemy with a smile before they overwhelm us; as they will, of course. Like me, the candle is mortal; it will burn out.

As the bed-book itself should be a sort of nightlight, to assist its illumination, coarse lamps are useless. They would douse the book. The light for such a book must accord with it. It must be, like the book, a limited, personal, mellow, and companionable glow; the solitary taper beside the only worshipper in a sanctuary. That is why nothing can compare with the intimacy of candle-

Bed-Books and Night-Lights

light for a bed-book. It is a living heart, bright
and warm in central night, burning for us alone,
holding the gaunt and towering shadows at bay.
There the monstrous spectres stand in our midnight room, the advance guard of the darkness of
the world, held off by our valiant little glim, but
ready to flood instantly and founder us in original
gloom.

The wind moans without; ancient evils are at
large and wandering in torment. The rain
shrieks across the window. For a moment, for
just a moment, the sentinel candle is shaken, and
burns blue with terror. The shadows leap out
instantly. The little flame recovers, and merely
looks at its foe the darkness, and back to its own
place goes the old enemy of light and man. The
candle for me, tiny, mortal, warm, and brave, a
golden lily on a silver stem!

"Almost any book does for a bed-book," a
woman once said to me. I nearly replied in a
hurry that almost any woman would do for a
wife; but that is not the way to bring people to
conviction of sin. Her idea was that the bed-
book is a soporific, and for that reason she even
advocated the reading of political speeches.
That would be a dissolute act. Certainly you
would go to sleep; but in what a frame of mind!

[67]

Old Junk

You would enter into sleep with your eyes shut. It would be like dying, not only unshriven, but in the act of guilt.

What book shall it shine upon? Think of Plato, or Dante, or Tolstoy, or a Blue Book for such an occasion! I cannot. They will not do — they are no good to me. I am not writing about you. I know those men I have named are transcendent, the greater lights. But I am bound to confess at times they bore me. Though their feet are clay and on earth, just as ours, their stellar brows are sometimes dim in remote clouds. For my part, they are too big for bed-fellows. I cannot see myself, carrying my feeble and restricted glim, following (in pyjamas) the statuesque figure of the Florentine where it stalks, aloof in its garb of austere pity, the sonorous deeps of Hades. Hades! Not for me; not after midnight! Let those go who like it.

As for the Russian, vast and disquieting, I refuse to leave all, including the blankets and the pillow, to follow him into the gelid tranquillity of the upper air, where even the colours are prismatic spicules of ice, to brood upon the erratic orbit of the poor mud-ball below called earth. I know it is my world also; but I cannot help that. It is too late, after a busy day, and at that hour, to

Bed-Books and Night-Lights

begin overtime on fashioning a new and better planet out of cosmic dust. By breakfast-time, nothing useful would have been accomplished. We should all be where we were the night before. The job is far too long, once the pillow is nicely set.

For the truth is, there are times when we are too weary to remain attentive and thankful under the improving eye, kindly but severe, of the seers. There are times when we do not wish to be any better than we are. We do not wish to be elevated and improved. At midnight, away with such books! As for the literary pundits, the high priests of the Temple of Letters, it is interesting and helpful occasionally for an acolyte to swinge them a good hard one with an incense-burner, and cut and run, for a change, to something outside the rubrics. Midnight is the time when one can recall, with ribald delight, the names of all the Great Works which every gentleman ought to have read, but which some of us have not. For there is almost as much clotted nonsense written about literature as there is about theology.

There are few books which go with midnight, solitude, and a candle. It is much easier to say

Old Junk

what does not please us then than what is exactly right. The book must be, anyhow, something benedictory by a sinning fellow-man. Cleverness would be repellent at such an hour. Cleverness, anyhow, is the level of mediocrity today; we are all too infernally clever. The first witty and perverse paradox blows out the candle. Only the sick in mind crave cleverness, as a morbid body turns to drink. The late candle throws its beams a great distance; and its rays make transparent much that seemed massy and important. The mind at rest beside that light, when the house is asleep, and the consequential affairs of the urgent world have diminished to their right proportions because we see them distantly from another and a more tranquil place in the heavens where duty, honour, witty arguments, controversial logic on great questions, appear such as will leave hardly a trace of fossil in the indurated mud which presently will cover them — the mind then certainly smiles at cleverness.

For though at that hour the body may be dog-tired, the mind is white and lucid, like that of a man from whom a fever has abated. It is bare of illusions. It has a sharp focus, small and star-like, as a clear and lonely flame left burning by the altar of a shrine from which all have gone but one. A book which approaches that light in the privacy of that place must come, as it were, with honest and open pages.

I like Heine then, though. His mockery of the grave and great, in those sentences which are as brave as pennants in a breeze, is comfortable and sedative. One's own secret and awkward convictions, never expressed because not lawful and because it is hard to get words to bear them lightly, seem then to be heard aloud in the mild, easy, and confident diction of an immortal whose voice has the blitheness of one who has watched, amused and irreverent, the high gods in eager and secret debate on the best way to keep the gilt and trappings on the body of the evil they have created.

That first-rate explorer, Gulliver, is also fine in the light of the intimate candle. Have you read lately again his Voyage to the Houyhnhnms? Try it alone again in quiet. Swift knew all about our contemporary troubles. He has got it all down. Why was he called a misanthrope? Reading that last voyage of Gulliver in the select intimacy of midnight I am forced to wonder, not at Swift's hatred of mankind, not at his satire of his fellows, not at the strange and terrible nature

[71]

Old Junk

of this genius who thought that much of us, but how it is that after such a wise and sorrowful revealing of the things we insist on doing, and our reasons for doing them, and what happens after we have done them, men do not change. It does seem impossible that society could remain unaltered, after the surprise its appearance should have caused it as it saw its face in that ruthless mirror. We point instead to the fact that Swift lost his mind in the end. Well, that is not a matter for surprise.

Such books, and France's *Isle of Penguins*, are not disturbing as bed-books. They resolve one's agitated and outraged soul, relieving it with some free expression for the accusing and questioning thoughts engendered by the day's affairs. But they do not rest immediately to hand in the bookshelf by the bed. They depend on the kind of day one has had. Sterne is closer. One would rather be transported as far as possible from all the disturbances of earth's envelope of clouds, and *Tristram Shandy* is sure to be found in the sun.

But best of all books for midnight are travel books. Once I was lost every night for months with Doughty in the *Arabia Deserta*. He is a craggy author. A long course of the ordinary

Bed-Books and Night-Lights

facile stuff, such as one gets in the Press every day, thinking it is English, sends one thoughtless and headlong among the bitter herbs and stark boulders of Doughty's burning and spacious expanse; only to get bewildered, and the shins broken, and a great fatigue at first, in a strange land of fierce sun, hunger, glittering spar, ancient plutonic rock, and very Adam himself. But once you are acclimatized, and know the language — it takes time — there is no more London after dark, till, a wanderer returned from a forgotten land, you emerge from the interior of Arabia on the Red Sea coast again, feeling as though you had lost touch with the world you used to know. And if that doesn't mean good writing I know of no other test.

Because once there was a father whose habit it was to read with his boys nightly some chapters of the Bible — and cordially they hated that habit of his — I have that Book too; though I fear I have it for no reason that he, the rigid old faithful, would be pleased to hear about. He thought of the future when he read the Bible; I read it for the past. The familiar names, the familiar rhythm of its words, its wonderful well-remembered stories of things long past, — like that of Esther, one of the best in English, — the eloquent anger of the prophets for the people then who looked as though they were alive, but were really dead at heart, all is solace and home to me.   And now I think of it, it is our home and solace that we want in a bed-book.

V.   Transfiguration

THERE it is, thirty miles wide between the horns of the land, a bay opening north-west upon the Atlantic, with a small island in the midst of the expanse, a heap of sundered granite lying upon the horizon like a faint sunken cloud, like the floating body of a whale, like an area of opalescent haze, like an inexplicable brightness at sea when no island can be seen. The apparition of that island depends upon the favour of the sun. The island is only a ghost there, sometimes invisible, sometimes but an alluring and immaterial fragment of the coast we see far over the sea in dreams; a vision of sanctuary, of the place we shall never reach, a frail mirage of land then, a roseous spot which is not set in the sea, but floats there only while the thought of a haven of peace and secure verities is still in the mind, and while the longing eye projects it on the horizon.

The sun sets behind the island. On a clear

Old Junk

day, at sundown, the island behaves so much like a lump of separated earth, a piece of the black world we know, that I can believe it is land, something to be found on the map, a place where I could get ashore, after toil and adventures. At sundown a low yellow planet marks its hiding-place.

If the island in the bay is usually but a coloured thought in the mind, a phantom and an unattainable refuge by day, and a star by night, the real coast which stretches seaward to it, marching on either hand into the blue, confident and tall, is hardly more material, except by the stones of my outlook. The near rocks are of indubitable earth.

Beyond them the coloured fabric of the bay becomes diaphanous, and I can but wonder at the permanence of such a coast in this wind, for in it the delicate cliffs and the frail tinted fields inclined above them seem to tremble, as though they would presently collapse and tear from their places and stream inland as torn flimsies and gossamer.

It is the sublimation of earth. Our own shining globe floats with the others in a sea of light. Here in the bay on a September morning, if our world till then had been without life and voice, with this shine that is an impalpable dust of

Transfiguration

gold, the quickened air, and the seas moving as though joyous in the first dawn, Eros and Aurora would have known the moment, and a child would have been born.

None but the transcendent and mounting qualities of our elements, and the generative day which makes the surf dazzling, and draws the passionate azure of the bugloss from hot and arid sand, and makes the blobs of sea-jelly in the pools expand like flowers, and ripens the clouds, nothing but the indestructible essence of life, life uplifted and dominant, shows now in this world of the bay.

Below the high moors which enclose the bay, those distant sleepy uplands where the keels of the cumulus clouds are grounded, there are saline meadows, lush and warm, where ditches serpentine between barriers of meadowsweet, briers and fat grasses. Nearer to the sea the levels are of moist sand covered with a close matting of thyme, and herbage as close and resilient as moss, levels that are not green, like fields, but golden, and of a texture that reflects the light, so that these plains seem to have their own brightness.

The sea plains finish in the sandhills. In this desert you may press a hand into the body of earth, and feel its heat and pulse. The west wind pours among the dunes, a warm and heavy torrent.

Old Junk

There is no need to make a miracle of the appearance of life on our earth. Life was at the happy incidence of the potent elements on such a strand as this. Aphrodite was no myth. Our mother here gave birth to her.

The sea is kept from the dunes by a high ridge of blue water-worn pebbles, and beyond the pebbles at low water is the wet strand over which she came wading to give the earth children in her own likeness. The Boy and Miss Muffet beside me are no surprise. They are proper to the place. The salt water and the sand are still on their brown limbs, and in the Boy's serious eyes and Miss Muffet's smile there is something outside my knowledge; but I know that in the depth of that mystery is security and content.

There is a fear I have, though, when they trip it over the solid and unquestionable stones, and leave the stones to fly off into the wind down that shining entrance to the deep. For the strand has no substance. Their feet move over a void in which far down I see another sky than ours. They go where I doubt that I can follow. I cannot leave my hold upon the rocks and enter the place to which their late and aerial spirits are native. It is plain the earth is not a solid body. As their bodies, moving over the bright vacuity,

Transfiguration

grow unsubstantial and elfin with distance, and
they approach that line where the surf glimmers
athwart the radiant void, I have a sudden fear
that they may vanish quite, and only their laughter
come at me mockingly from the near invisible air.
They will have gone back to their own place.

VI. The Pit Mouth

THERE was Great Barr, idle, still, and
quiet. Through the Birmingham sub-
urbs, out into the raw, bleak winter roads
between the hedges, quite beyond the big town
smoking with its enterprising labours, one approached the village of calamity with some awe
and diffidence. You felt you were intruding;
that you were a mere gross interloper, coming
through curiosity, that was not excused by the
compunction you felt, to see the appearance of a
place that had tragedy in nearly all its homes.
Young men streamed by on bicycles in the same
direction, groups were hurrying there on foot.

The road rose in a mound to let the railway
under, and beyond the far dip was the village,
an almost amorphous group of mean red dwellings stuck on ragged fields about the dominant
colliery buildings. Three high, slim chimneys
were leisurely pouring smoke from the grotesque
black skeleton structures above the pits. The
road ran by the boundary, and was packed with

[80]

The Pit Mouth

people, all gazing absorbed and quiet into the grounds of the colliery; they were stacked up the hedge banks, and the walls and trees were loaded with boys.

A few empty motor-cars of the colliery directors stood about. A carriage-horse champed its bit, and the still watchers turned at once to that intrusive sound. Around us, a lucid winter landscape (for it had been raining) ran to the distant encompassing hills which lifted like low ramparts of cobalt and amethyst to a sky of luminous saffron and ice-green, across which leaden clouds were moving. The country had that hard, coldly radiant appearance which always impresses a sad man as this world's frank expression of its alien disregard; this world not his, on which he has happened, and must endure with his trouble for a brief time.

As I went through the press of people to the colliery gates, the women in shawls turned to me, first with annoyance that their watching should be disturbed, and then with some dull interest. My assured claim to admittance probably made them think I was the bearer of new help outside their little knowledge; and they willingly made room for me to pass. I felt exactly like the interfering fraud I was. What would I not have

Old Junk

given then to be made, for a brief hour, a nameless miracle-worker.

In the colliery itself was the same seeming apathy. There was nothing to show in that yard, black with soddened cinders and ash muck, where the new red-brick engine-houses stood, that somewhere half a mile beneath our feet were thirty men, their only exit to the outer world barred by a subterranean fire. Nothing showed of the fire but a whitish smoke from a ventilating shaft; and a stranger would not know what that signified. But the women did. Wet with the rain showers, they had been standing watching that smoke all night, and were watching it still, for its unceasing pour to diminish. Constant and unrelenting, it streamed steadily upward, as though it drew its volume from central fires that would never cease.

The doors of the office were thrown open, and three figures emerged. They broke into the listlessness of that dreary place, where nothing seemed to be going on, with a sudden real purpose, fast but unhurried, and moved towards the shaft. Three Yorkshire rescue experts — one of them to die later — with the Hamstead manager explaining the path they should follow below with eager seriousness. " Figures of fun "! They had muzzles on their mouths and noses, goggles

The Pit Mouth

on their eyes, fantastic helms, and queer cylinders and bags slung about them. As they went up the slope of wet ash, quick and full of purpose, their comical gear and coarse dress became suddenly transfigured; and the silent crowd cheered emotionally that little party of forlorn hope.

They entered the cage, and down they went. Still it was difficult for me to think that we were fronting tragedy, for no danger showed. An hour and more passed in nervous and dismal waiting. There was a signal. Some men ran to the pit-head carrying hot bricks and blankets. The doctors took off their coats, and arranged bottles and tinkling apparatus on chairs stuck in the mud. The air smelt of iodoform. A cloth was laid on the ground from the shaft to the engine-house, and stretchers were placed handy. The women, some carrying infants, broke rank. That quickly up-running rope was bringing the first news. The rope stopped running and the cage appeared. Only the rescue party came out, one carrying a moribund cat. They knew nothing; and the white-faced women, with hardly repressed hysteria, took again their places by the engine-house. So we passed that day, watching the place from which came nothing but disappointment. Oc-

[83]

casionally a child, too young to know it was adding
to its mother's grief, would wail querulously.
There came a time when I and all there knew that
to go down that shaft was to meet with death.
The increasing exhaustion and pouring sweat of
the returning rescue parties showed that. Yet the
miners who were not selected to go down were
angry; they violently abused the favouritism of
the officials who would not let all risk their lives.

I have a new regard for my fellows since Great
Barr. About you and me there are men like that.
There is nothing to distinguish them. They show
no signs of greatness. They have common talk.
They have coarse ways. They walk with an ugly
lurch. Their eyes are not eager. They are not
polite. Their clothes are dirty. They live in
cheap houses on cheap food. They call you
" sir." They are the great unwashed, the mut-
able many, the common people. The common
people! Greatness is as common as that. There
are not enough honours and decorations to go
round. Talk of the soldier! *Vale* to Welsby of
Normanton! He was a common miner. He is
dead. His fellows were in danger, their wives
were white-faced and their children were crying,
and he buckled on his harness and went to the
assault with no more thought for self than great

The Pit Mouth

men have in a great cause; and he is dead.   I saw
him go to his death.   I wish I could tell you of
Welsby of Normanton.

I left that place where the star-shine was showing the grim skeleton of the shaft-work overhead
in the night, and where men moved about below in
the indeterminate dark like dismal gnomes.
There was a woman whose cry, when Welsby died,
was like a challenge.

Next morning, in Great Barr, some blinds
were down, the street was empty.   Children,
who could see no reason about them why their
fathers should not return as usual, were playing
foot-ball by the tiny church.   A group of women
were still gazing at the grotesque ribs and legs
of the pit-head staging as though it were a
monster without ruth.

November 1907.

VII. Initiation

AS to what the Boy will become, that is still with his stars; and though once we thought he was much impressed by the dignity of the man controlling a road roller, for it seemed it would be well to be that slow herald in front with a little red flag, he has shown but the faintest regard for the offices of policeman, engine-driver, and soldier. It is clear there is but one good thing left for his choice, and so the house is littered with drawings of ships. There has been some advance from that early affair of black angles which, without explanation, might have stood for anything, but was meant for a cutter. Now, in a manner which a careless visitor could think was the hauteur of an artist who is too sure of himself to care what you think of his work, but is really acute shyness, he will present you at short notice with a sketch in colours of a topsail schooner beating off a lee shore, if your variety of beard does not rouse his suspicion. As art, such paintings have their faults; but as delinea-

Initiation

tions of that sort of ship they have technical exactitude not common even in the studios.

In fact, he has found an old manual of seamanship, and the illustrations get more attention than some people give to Biblical subjects. During vacant afternoons there is an uncanny calm in the house, a silence which makes people think they have forgotten something important; but it is only that the Boy is absent with the argonauts. He is in tow of Argo, as it were, one of its heroes, surging astern in a large easy-chair, viewing golden landfalls that are still under their early spell in seas that ships have never sailed. There are no such voyages in later life, none with quite that glamour, for we have tried and know. Lucky Boy, sailing the greatest voyage of his life! Occasionally, when a real ship is home again, and some one calls to see if we still live there, the Boy is allowed to go to bed late, and there he sits and fills his mind.

"And what," said this deponent one evening, "about taking His Nibs with me?" (There was some sea to be crossed.) Most certainly not! Well —! still —! Would he be all right? But as he got to hear about this it was hardly so certainly not as it seemed. There are times when he can concentrate on a subject with awful

Old Junk

pertinacity, though the occasions are infrequent. This was one, however. He went. I knew he would go — when he heard about it.

A day came when we were at the railway station, and he was to cross the sea for the first time. He was quite collected. His quiet eye enumerated the baggage in one careless side-glance which detected there was a strap undone and that a walking-stick was missing. In all that crowded tumult converging on the stroke of the hour his seemed to be the only apart and impassive face, and I began to think he was indifferent; he merely looked at the cover of one magazine, and then turned to the window and observed the world leaping past with the detachment of a small immortal who was watching man's fleeting affairs. Nothing to do with him.

Once he caught my intent eye — for I thought he was a trifle pale — and then he passed a radiant wink, and one of his dangling legs began to swing as though that were the sole limb to be joyful. An hour later, his face still to the glass, he was shaking with internal mirth. I asked him to let me share it with him. " Did you see that old man at the station when the train was starting?" he whispered. "He couldn't find the carriage where his things were — he was

[88]

running up and down without a hat. Perhaps he
was left behind." What do man's misfortune's
matter to the gods who live for ever?

Through sections of the quayside sheds he
caught sight of near funnels, businesslike with
smoke, and a row of ports. It was then I had
to tell him there was plenty of time. "Two
funnels," I heard him say in surprise, and there
is no doubt at that moment some of the importance of the occasion was reflected on myself.
That extra funnel told him, I hope, I was doing
this business in no meagre spirit. None of your
single-funnel ships for our affairs. At the quay
end of the gangway he stopped me, interrupting
the whole concourse to do so. " Where's that
other bag? " he demanded severely. I was annoyed — like the people who were following us
— but I had to admire him all the same. At his
age no doubt it may be demanded that a ship be
put about for a bag left behind. When this
childish egoism is maintained well into life, large
fortunes may be made. It is, perhaps, the only
way. As soon as a man can relate his personal
affairs to those of the world, and understands
how unimportant he really is, from that moment
he becomes a failure. Some men never do it,

[89]

and thus succeed. Therefore I allowed the Boy
to lead me aboard, and so secured a good berth at
once, to the envy of those who were unaided by
a child. Already I was informed that, after
due inspection, the steamer had plenty of boats,
" so it won't matter if we sink." In five minutes
we had discovered the companions to everywhere
on that ship, and were, I believe, the only passengers who could find our way about her before
she left port.

But a glance seaward, and a word with an
officer, gave me a thought or two, and I broke off
the Boy's interesting conversation with a fatherly
French quartermaster to take him where he could
at least begin with some food. " What a lark
if there's a storm," laughed His Nibs, removing
a sandwich to say so. The fiddles were on the
tables. We were off.

The ship gave a lurch, a ham leaped to the
floor, some plates crashed, and then the row of
ports alongside us were darkened by the run of
a wave. The Boy made an exclamation partly
stifled, and looked at me quickly. I did not look
at him, but went on with the food. He stopped
eating, and remained with his gaze fixed on the
ports, gripping his chair whenever they went

Initiation

dark. He said nothing about it, but he must have been thinking pretty hard. "I suppose this is a strong ship, isn't it?" he questioned once.

As we were about to emerge into the open, the wet, deserted deck fell away, and a grey wave which looked as aged as death, its white hair streaming in the wind, suddenly reared over the ship's side, as though looking for us, and then fled phantom-like, with dire cries. The Boy shrank back for a moment, horrified, but then moved on. I think I heard him sigh. It was no summer sea. The dark bales of rain were speeding up from the south-west, low over waters which looked just what the sea really is.

I am glad he saw it like that. He hung on in a shelter with a needlessly tight grip, and there was something of consternation in his eye. But I enjoyed the cry of surprise he gave once when we were getting used to it. A schooner passed us, quite close, a midget which fairly danced over the running hills, lifting her bows and soaring upwards, light as a bird, and settling in the hollows amid a white cloud. "Isn't she brave!" said the Boy.

December 1910

VIII. The Art of Writing

WHETHER I placed the writing-pad on my knees in a great chair, or on the table, or on the floor, nothing happened to it. I can only say that that morning the paper was full of vile hairs, which the pen kept getting into its mouth — enough to ruin the goodwill of any pen. Yet all the circumstances of the room seemed luckily placed for work to flow with ease; but there was some mysterious and inimical obstruction. The fire was bright and lively, the familiar objects about the table appeared to be in their right place. Again I examined the gods of the table to be sure one had not by mischance broken the magic circle and interrupted the current of favour for me. They were rightly orientated — that comic pebble paper-weight Miss Muffet found on the beach of a distant holiday, the chrysanthemums which were fresh from that very autumn morning, stuck in the blue vase which must have got its colour in the Gulf Stream; and

[92]

The Art of Writing

the rusty machete blade from Peru, and the earthenware monkey squatting meekly in his shadowy niche, holding the time in his hands. The time was going on, too.

I tried all the tricks I knew for getting under way, but the pen continued to do nothing but draw idle faces and pick up hairs, which it held firmly in its teeth. Then the second telegram was brought to me. " What about Balkan article? " it asked, and finished with a studied insult, after the manner of the editor-kind, whose assurance that the function of the universe is only fulfilled when they have published the fact makes them behave as would Jove with a thick-headed immortal. " These Balkan atrocities will never cease," I said, dropping the telegram into the fire.

Had I possessed but one of those intelligent manuals which instruct the innocent in the art, not only of writing, but of writing so well that a very disappointed and world-weary editor rejoices when he sees the manuscript, puts his thumbs up and calls for wine, I would have consulted it. (I should be glad to hear if there is such a book, with a potent remedy for just common dulness — the usual opaque, gummous, slow, thick, or fat head.) As for me, I have nothing but a cheap dictionary, and that I could not find. I raised my voice, calling down the hollow, dusty, and unfurnished spaces of my mind, summoning my servants, my carefully chosen but lazy and wilful staff of words, to my immediate aid. But there was no answer; only the cobwebs moved there, though I thought I heard a faint buzzing, which might have been a blow-fly. No doubt my staff — small blame to them — were dreaming somewhere in the sun, dispersed over several seas and continents.

Well, a suburb of a big town, and such jobs as I find for them to do, are grey enough for them in winter. I have no doubt some were nooning it in Algiers, and others were prospecting the South Seas, flattering themselves, with gross vanity, how well they could serve me there, if only I would give them a chance with those coloured and lonely islands; and others were in the cabins of ships far from any land, gossiping about old times; and these last idle words, it is my experience, are the most stubborn of the lot, usually ignoring all my efforts to get them home again and to business. I could call and rage as I chose, or entreat them, showing them the urgency of my need. But only a useless and indefinite article came along, as he usually does, hours and hours before the arrival of a lusty

The Art of Writing

word which could throw about the suggestions quicker than they may be picked up and examined.

Very well. There was nothing for it but to fill another pipe, and dwell with some dismay upon such things as, for instance, the way one's light grows smoky with age. Is there a manual which will help a man to keep his light shining brightly — supposing he has a light to keep? But if he has but the cheapest of transient glims, good and bright enough for its narrow purpose, is it any wonder it burns foul, seeing what business usually it gets to illuminate in these exciting and hurried times. What work! I think it would make rebels of the most quiet, unadventurous, and simple-featured troop of words that ever a man gathered about him for the plain domestic duties to employ them regularly, for example, in sweeping up into neat columns such litter as the House of Commons makes. It would numb the original heart of the bonniest set of words that rightly used would have made some people happy — sterilize them, make them anaemic and pasty-faced, so that they would disturb the peace of mind of all compassionate men who looked upon them. That my own staff of words refused my summons . . .

But what was it I said I wanted them for just

[95]

Old Junk

now? I gazed round the walls upon the portraits of the great writers of the past, hoping for inspiration. Useless! Upon Emerson's face there was a faint smile of most infuriating benevolence. Lamb — but I am getting tired of his smirk, which might be of irony or kindness. He would look savage enough today, hearing his constantly returning Dissertation on Roast Pig thump the door-mat four times a week; for that, he can be assured, is the way editors would treat it now, and without even preliminary consultations with lady typist-secretaries. Of the whole gallery of the great I felt there was not one worth his wall room. They are pious frauds. This inspiration business is played out. I have never had the worth of the frames out of those portraits. . . . Ah, the Balkans. That was it. And of all the flat, interminable Arctic wastes of bleak wickedness and frozen error that ever a shivering writer had to traverse . . .

My head was in my hands, and I was trying to get daylight and direction into the affair with my eyes shut, when I felt a slight touch on my arm. "I'm sorry we're in your way. Are you praying? Look who's here."

I looked. It was Miss Muffet who spoke. She shook the gold out of her eyes and regarded

[96]

me steadily. Well she knew she had no right there, for all her look of confident and tender solicitude. The Boy, who is a little older (and already knows enough to place the responsibility for intrusion on his sister with her innocent eyes and imperturbable calm and golden hair), stood a little in the background, pretending to be engrossed with a magnet, as though he were unaware that he was really present. Curls hopped about on one leg frankly, knowing that the others would be blamed for any naughtiness of hers. Her radiant impudence never needs any apology. What a plague of inconsequential violators of any necessary peace! When would my lucky words come now?

The Boy probably saw a red light somewhere. " Haven't you finished uncle we thought you had has a topsail schooner got two or three masts I saw a fine little engine up in the town today and an aeroplane it was only seventeen shillings do you think that is too much? "

" I am learning the sailors' hornpipe at school," said Miss Muffet, slowly and calmly; " you watch my feet. Do I dance it nicely? "

I watched her feet. Now it is but fair to say that when Miss Muffet dances across a room there is no international crisis in all this world

Old Junk

which would distract any man's frank admiration.
When Miss Muffet steps it on a sunny day, her
hair being what it is, and her little feet in her
strap shoes being such as they are, then your mood
dances in accord, and your thoughts swing in
light and rythmic harmony. I got up. And
Curls, who is one of those who must mount stairs
laboriously, secure to the rails — she has black
eyes only the bright light of which is seen through
her mane — she reached up for my hand, for she
cannot imitate her sister's hornpipe without holding on.

Miss Muffet reached a corner of the room, and
swung round, light as a fairy, her hands on her
hips, and said, "What do you think of that?"
Some of my lucky words instantly returned. I
suppose it was more to their mind. But I had
nothing to give them to do. They could just
stand around and look on now, for when Curls
seriously imitates her sister, and then laughs
heartily at her own absurd failure, because her feet
are irresponsible, that is the time when you have
nothing to do, and would not do anything if it
had to be done. . . .

What time it was the next interruption came —
it was another telegram — I don't know. Time
had been obliterated. But then it began to flow

The Art of Writing

again; though not with a viscid and heavy measure. And when I took up my light and ready pen, there, standing at eager attention, was all my staff, waiting the call. What had happened to bring them all back? If the writers of literary manuals will explain that secret to me, I should acquire true wealth.

IX. A First Impression

CERTAINLY it was an inconsiderate way of approaching the greatest city of the Americas, but that was not my fault. I wished for the direct approach, the figure of Liberty to rise, haughty and most calm, a noble symbol, as we came in from overseas; then the wide portals; then New York. But the erratic tracks of a tramp steamer go not as her voyagers will. They have no control over her. She moves to an enigmatic will in London. It happens, then, that she rarely shows a wonder of the world any respect. She arrives like sudden rain, like wind from a new quarter. She is as chance as the fall of a star. None knows the day nor the hour. At the most inconvenient time she takes the wonder's visitors to the back door.

We went, light ship from the South, to Barbados, for orders; and because I wanted New York, for that was the way home, we were sent to Tampa for phosphates. As to Tampa, its position on the globe is known only to under-

A First Impression

writers and shipbrokers; it is that sort of place.
It is a mere name, like Fernando de Noronha, or
Key West, which one meets only in the shipping
news, idly wondering then what strange things
the seafarer would find if he went.

Late one night, down a main street of Tampa,
there came, with the deliberate movement of
fate, a gigantic corridor train, looming as high
as a row of lighted villas, and drawn by the awful
engine of a dream. That train behaved there as
trams do at home, presently stopping alongside
a footway.

Behind me was a little wooden shop. In front
was the wall of a carriage, having an entrance on
the second storey, and a roof athwart the me-
ridian stars. One of its wheels was the nearest
and most dominant object in the night to me, a
monstrous bright round resting on a muddy newspaper in the road. It absorbed all the light from
the little wooden shop. Now, I had hunted
throughout Tampa for its railway terminus, fruit-
lessly; but here its train had found me, keeping
me from crossing the road.

"Where do I board this train for New
York?" I asked. (I talked like a fool, I know;
it was like asking a casual wayfarer in East Ham
whether that by the kerb is the Moscow express.

Old Junk

Yet what was I to do?) " Board her right here," said the fellow, who was in his shirt sleeves. Therefore I delivered myself, in blind faith, to the casual gods who are apt to wake up and by a series of deft little miracles get things done fitly in America when all seems lost and the traveller has even bared his resigned neck to the stroke.

But I had not the least hope of seeing New York and a Cunarder; not with such an unpropitious start as that. With an exit like Euston one never doubts sure direction, and arrival at the precise spot at the exact moment. You feel there it was arranged for in Genesis. The officials cannot alter affairs. They are priests administering inviolate rites, advancing matters fore-ordained by the unseen, and so no more able to stay or speed this cosmic concern than the astronomer who schedules the planets. The planets take their heavenly courses. But I had never been to the United States before, did not know even the names of their many gods, and New York was at the end of a great journey; and the train for it stopped outside a tobacco shop in the road, like a common tram.

There was another night when, with the usual unreason, the swift and luxurious glide, lessening

[102]

A First Impression

through easy gradations, ceased. I saw some lights in the rain outside. How should I know it was New York? We had even changed climates since we started. The passengers of my early days in the train had passed away. There was nothing to show. More, I felt no exultation — which should have been the first of warnings. Merely we got to a railway station one night, and a negro insisted that I should get out and stop out. This was N' Yark, he said.

It was night, I repeat; there was a row of cabs in a dolorous rain. I saw a man in a shiny cape under the nearest lamp, and beyond him a vista of reflections from vacant stones, which to me always, more than bleak hills or the empty round of the sea, is desolation. There were no spacious portals. There was no figure of Liberty, haughty but welcoming. There was rain, and cabs that waited without hope. There was exactly what you find at the end of a twopenny journey when your only luggage is an evening paper, an umbrella, and that tired feeling. Not knowing where to go, and little caring, I followed the crowd, and so found myself in a large well-lighted hall. Having no business there — it was a barren place — I pushed on, and came suddenly to the rim of the world.

Old Junk

Before me was the immensity of dark celestial space in which wandered hosts of uncharted stars; and below my feet was the abyss of old night. Just behind me was a woman telling her husband that they had forgotten Jimmy's boots, and couldn't go back now, for the ferry was just coming.

Jimmy's boots! Now, when you are a released soul, ascending the night, and the earth below is a bright silver ball, not so very big, and some other viewless soul behind you, still with thoughts absent on worldly trifles, mutters concerning boots when in the Milky Way, you will know how I felt. Here was the ultimate empty dark in which the sun could never shine. The sun had not merely left the place. It had never been there. It was a remote star, one of myriads in the constellations at large, the definite groups which occulted in the void before me. Looking at those swiftly moving systems, I watched for the fla t of impact; but no great light of collision bro The groups of lights passed and repassed r iselessly.

Then one constellation presently detached itself, and its orbit evidently would intersect our foothold. It came nearer out of the night, till I could see plainly that it appeared to be a long section of a well-lighted street, say, like a length

A First Impression

of Piccadilly. It approached end-on to where I stood, and at last impinged. It actually was a length of street, and I could continue my walk. The street floated off again into the night, with me, Jimmy's father and mother, and all of us, and the vans and motor-cars; and the other square end of it soon joined a roadway on the opposite shore. The dark river was as full of mobile lengths of bright roadway as Oxford Circus is of motor-buses; and the fear of the unknown, as in the terrific dark of a dream where flaming comets stream on undirected courses, numbed my little mind. I had found New York.

I had found it. Its bulk was beyond the mind, its lights were falling star systems, and its movements those of general cataclysm. I should find no care for little human needs there. One cannot warm one's hands against the flames of earthquake. There is no provision for men in the welter, but dimly apprehended in the night, of blind and inhuma owers.

Therefore, the otel bedroom, when I got to it, surprised and steadied me with its elaborate care for the body. But yet I was not certain. Then I saw against the wall a dial, and reading a notice over it I learned that by working the hands of this false clock correctly I could procure anything, from an apple to the fire brigade. Now this was carrying matters to the other extreme; and I had to suppress a desire to laugh hysterically. I set the hands to a number; waited one minute; then the door opened, and a waiter came in with a real tray, conveying a glass and a bottle. So there was a method then in this general madness after all. I tried to regard the wonder as indifferently as the waiter's own cold and measuring eyes.

March 1910.

X.   The Derelict

IN a tramp steamer, which was overloaded, and in midwinter, I had crossed to America for the first time.   What we experienced of the western ocean during that passage gave me so much respect for it that the prospect of the return journey, three thousand miles of those seas between me and home, was already a dismal foreboding.   The shipping posters of New York, showing stately liners too lofty even to notice the Atlantic, were arguments good enough for steerage passengers, who do, I know, reckon a steamer's worth by the number of its funnels; but the pictures did nothing to lessen my regard for that dark outer world I knew.   And having no experience of ships installed with racquet courts, Parisian cafés, swimming baths, and pergolas, I was naturally puzzled by the inconsequential behaviour of the first-class passengers at the hotel. They were leaving by the liner which was to take me, and, I gathered, were going to cross a bridge to England in the morning.   Of course, this might have been merely the innocent profanity of the simple-minded.

Embarking at the quay next day, I could not see that our ship had either a beginning or an end. There was a blank wall which ran out of sight to the right and left. How far it went, and what it enclosed, were beyond me. Hundreds of us in a slow procession mounted stairs to the upper floor of a warehouse, and from thence a bridge led us to a door in the wall half-way in its height. No funnels could be seen. Looking straight up from the embarkation gangway, along what seemed the parapet of the wall was a row of far-off indistinguishable faces peering straight down at us. There was no evidence that this building we were entering, of which the high black wall was a part, was not an important and permanent feature of the city. It was in keeping with the magnitude of New York's skyscrapers, which this planet's occasionally non-irritant skin permits to stand there to afford man an apparent reason to be gratified with his own capacity and daring.

But with the knowledge that this wall must be afloat there came no sense of security when, going through that little opening in its altitude, I found myself in a spacious decorated interior which hinted nothing of a ship, for I was puzzled as

The Derelict

to direction. My last ship could be surveyed in two glances; she looked, and was, a comprehensible ship, no more than a manageable handful for an able master. In that ship you could see at once where you were and what to do. But in this liner you could not see where you were, and would never know which way to take unless you had a good memory. No understanding came to me in that hall of a measured and shapely body, designed with a cunning informed by ages of sea-lore to move buoyantly and surely among the ranging seas, to balance delicately, a quick and sensitive being, to every precarious slope, to recover a lost poise easily and with the grace natural to a quick creature controlled by an alert mind.

There was no shape at all to this structure. I could see no line the run of which gave me warrant that it was comprised in the rondure of a ship. The lines were all of straight corridors, which, for all I knew, might have ended blindly on open space, as streets which traverse a city and are bare in vacancy beyond the dwellings. It was possible we were encompassed by walls, but only one wall was visible. There we idled, all strangers, and to remain strangers, in a large hall roofed by a dome of coloured glass. Quite properly, palms stood beneath. There were offices and doors everywhere. On a broad staircase a multitude of us wandered aimlessly up and down. Each side of the stairway were electric lifts, intermittent and brilliant apparitions. I began to understand why the saloon passengers thought nothing of the voyage. They were encountering nothing unfamiliar. They had but come to another hotel for a few days.

I attempted to find my cabin, but failed. A uniformed guide took care of me. But my cabin, curtained, upholstered, and warm, with mirrors and plated ware, sunk somewhere deeply among carpeted and silent streets down each of which the perspective of glow-lamps looked interminable, left me still questioning. The long walk had given me a fear that I was remote from important affairs which might be happening beyond. My address was 323. The street door — I was down a side turning, though — bore that number. A visitor could make no mistake, supposing he could find the street and my side turning. That was it There was a very great deal in this place for everybody to remember, and most of us were strangers. No doubt, however, we were afloat, if the lifebelts in the rack meant anything. Yet the cabin, insulated from all noise, was not soothing, but disturbing. I had been used to a ship in

The Derelict

which you could guess all that was happening
even when in your bunk; a sensitive and commun-
icative ship.

A steward appeared at my door, a stranger
out of nowhere, and asked whether I had seen a
bag not mine in the cabin. He might have been
created merely to put that question, for I never
saw him again on the voyage. This liner was
a large province having irregular and shifting
bounds, permitting incontinent entrance and dis-
appearance. All this should have inspired me
with an idea of our vastness and importance, but
it did not. I felt I was one of a multitude included in a nebulous mass too vague to hold together unless we were constantly wary.

In the saloon there was the solid furniture of
rare woods, the ornate decorations, and the light
and shadows making vague its limits and giving
it an appearance of immensity, to keep the mind
from the thought of our real circumstances. At
dinner we had valentine music, dreamy stuff to
accord with the shaded lamps which displayed the
tables in a lower rosy light. It helped to extend
the mysterious and romantic shadows. The pale,
disembodied masks of the waiters swam in the
dusk above the tinted light. I had for a companion a vivacious American lady from the Middle

Old Junk

West, and she looked round that prospect we had of an expensive café, and said, " Well, but I am disappointed. Why, I've been looking forward to seeing the ocean, you know. And it isn't here."

" Smooth passage," remarked a man on the other side. " No sea at all worth mentioning." Actually, I know there was a heavy beam sea running before a half-gale. I could guess the officer in charge somewhere on the exposed roof might have another mind about it; but it made no difference to us in our circle of rosy intimate light bound by those vague shadows which were alive with ready servitude.

" And I've been reading *Captains Courageous* with this voyage in view. Isn't this the month when the forties roar? I want to hear them roar, just once, you know, and as gently as any sucking dove." We all laughed. " We can't even tell we're in a ship."

She began to discuss Kipling's book. " There's some fine seas in that. Have you read it? But I'd like to know where that ocean is he pretends to have seen. I do believe the realists are no more reliable than the romanticists. Here we are a thousand miles out, and none of us has seen the sea yet. Tell me, does not a realist have to

The Derelict

magnify his awful billows just to get them into
his reader's view? "

I murmured something feeble and sociable.
I saw then why sailors never talk directly of the
sea. I, for instance, could not find my key at that
moment — it was in another pocket somewhere
— so I had no iron to touch. Talking largely
of the sea is something like the knowing talk of
young men about women; and what is a simple
sailor man that he should open his mouth on mysteries?

Only on the liner's boat-deck, where you could
watch her four funnels against the sky, could you
see to what extent the liner was rolling. The arc
seemed to be considerable then, but slowly described. But the roll made little difference to
the promenaders below. Sometimes they walked
a short distance on the edges of their boots, leaning over as they did so, and swerving from the
straight, as though they had turned giddy. The
shadows formed by the weak sunlight moved
slowly out of ambush across the white deck, but
often moved indecisively, as though uncertain of
a need to go; and then slowly went into hiding
again. The sea whirling and leaping past was far
below our wall side. It was like peering dizzily

over a precipice when watching those green and white cataracts.

The passengers, wrapped and comfortable on the lee deck, chatted as blithely as at a garden-party, while the band played medleys of national airs to suit our varied complexions. The stewards came round with loaded trays. A diminutive and wrinkled dame in costly furs frowned through her golden spectacles at her book, while her maid sat attentively by. An American actress was the centre of an eager group of grinning young men; she was unseen, but her voice was distinct. The two Vanderbilts took their brisk constitutional among us as though the liner had but two real passengers though many invisible nobodies. The children, who had not ceased laughing and playing since we left New York, waited for the slope of the deck to reach its greatest, and then ran down towards the bulwarks precipitously. The children, happy and innocent, completed for us the feeling of comfortable indifference and security which we found when we saw there was more ship than ocean. The liner's deck canted slowly to leeward, went over more and more, beyond what it had done yet, and a pretty little girl with dark curls riotous from under her red tam-o'-shanter, ran down, and brought up against us

The Derelict

violently with both hands, laughing heartily. We laughed too. Looking seawards, I saw receding the broad green hill, snow-capped, which had lifted us and let us down. The sea was getting up.

Near sunset, when the billows were mounting express along our run, sometimes to leap and snatch at our upper structure, and were rocking us with some ease, there was a commotion forward. Books and shawls went anywhere as the passengers ran. Something strange was to be seen upon the waters.

It looked like a big log out there ahead, over the starboard bow. It was not easy to make out. The light was failing. We overhauled it rapidly, and it began to shape as a ship's boat. " Oh, it's gone," exclaimed some one then. But the forlorn object lifted high again, and sank once more. Whenever it was glimpsed it was set in a patch of foam.

That flotsam, whatever it was, was of man. As we watched it intently, and before it was quite plain, we knew intutively that hope was not there, that we were watching something past its doom. It drew abeam, and we saw what it was, a derelict sailing ship, mastless and awash. The alien wilderness was around us now, and we saw a sky that

[115]

was overcast and driven, and seas that were uplifted, which had grown incredibly huge, swift, and
perilous, and they had colder and more sombre
hues.

The derelict was a schooner, a lifeless and
soddened hulk, so heavy and uncontesting that its
foundering seemed at hand. The waters poured
back and forth at her waist, as though holding
her body captive for the assaults of the active
seas which came over her broken bulwarks, and
plunged ruthlessly about. There was something
ironic in the indifference of her defenceless body
to these unending attacks. It mocked this white
and raging post-mortem brutality, and gave her
a dignity that was cold and superior to all the
eternal powers could now do. She pitched help-
lessly head first into a hollow, and a door flew
open under the break of her poop; it surprised and
shocked us, for the dead might have signed to us
then. She went astern of us fast, and a great
comber ran at her, as if it had but just spied her,
and thought she was escaping. There was a high
white flash, and a concussion we heard. She had
gone. But she appeared again far away, on a
summit in desolation, black against the sunset.
The stump of her bowsprit, the accusatory finger
of the dead, pointed at the sky.

The Derelict

I turned, and there beside me was the lady who had wanted to find the sea. She was gazing at the place where the wreck was last seen, her eyes fixed, her mouth a little open in awe and horror.

April 1910.

XI. The Voyage of the *Mona*

THERE was the *Mona,* Yeo's boat, below the quay wall; but I could not see her owner. The unequal stones of that wall have the weathered appearance of a natural outcrop of rock, for they were matured by the traffic of ships when America was a new yarn among sailors. They are the very stones one would choose to hear speak. Yet the light of early morning in that spacious estuary was so young and tenuous that you could suppose this heavy planet had not yet known the stains of night and evil; and the *Mona,* it must be remembered, is white without and egg-blue within. Such were the reflections she made, lively at anchor on the swirls of a flood-tide bright enough for the sea-bottom to have been luminous, that I felt I must find Yeo. The white houses of the village, with shining faces, were looking out to sea.

Another man, a visitor from the cities of the plains, was gazing down with appreciation at the *Mona.* There was that to his credit. His young

The Voyage of the *Mona*

wife, slight and sad, and in the dress of the prom-
enade of a London park, was with him. She was
not looking on the quickness of the lucent tide,
but at the end of a parasol, which was idly mark-
ing the grits. I had seen the couple about the
village for a week. He was big, ruddy, middle-
aged, and lusty. His neck ran straight up into
his round head, and its stiff prickles glittered like
short ends of brass wire. It was easy to guess
of him, without knowing him and therefore un-
fairly, that, if his wife actually confessed to him
that she loved another man, he would not have
believed her; because how was it possible for her
to do that, he being what he was? His aggressive face, and his air of confident possession, the
unconscious immodesty of the man because of
his important success at some unimportant thing
or other, seemed an offence in the ancient tranquillity of that place, where poor men acknowl-
edged only the sea, the sun, and the winds.

I found Yeo at the end of the quay, where round
the corner to seaward open out the dunes of the
opposite shore of the estuary, faint with distance
and their own pallor, and ending in the slender
stalk of a lighthouse, always quivering at the vastness of what confronts it. Yeo was sitting on a
bollard, rubbing tobacco between his palms. I

told him this was the sort of morning to get the *Mona* out.   He carefully poured the grains into the bowl of his pipe, stoppered it, glanced slowly about the brightness of the river mouth, and shook his head.   This was a great surprise, and anybody who did not know Yeo would have questioned him.   But it was certain he knew his business.   There is not a more deceptive and difficult stretch of coast round these islands, and Yeo was born to it.   He stood up, and his long black hair stirred in the breeze under the broad brim of a grey hat he insists on wearing.   The soft hat and his lank hair make him womanish in profile, in spite of a body to which a blue jersey does full justice, and the sea-boots; but when he turns his face to you, with his light eyes and his dark and leathery face, you feel he is strangely masculine and wise, and must be addressed with care and not as most men.   He rarely smiles when a foolish word is spoken or when he is contradicted boldly by the innocent.   He spits at his feet and contemplates the sea, as though he had heard nothing.

The visitor came up, followed reluctantly by his wife.   "Are you Yeo?   How are you, Yeo? What about a sail?   I want you to take us round to Pebblecombe."

That village is over the bar and across the

The Voyage of the *Mona*

bay. Yeo looked at the man, and shook his head.

"Why not?" asked the visitor sharply, as though he were addressing the reluctance of the driver of his own car.

The sailor pointed a stern finger seawards, to where the bar is shown in charts, but where all we could make out was the flashing of inconstant white lines.

"Well?" questioned the man, who glanced out there perfunctorily. "What of it?"

"Look at it," mildly insisted the sailor, speaking for the first time. "Isn't the sea like a wall?" The man's wife, who was regarding Yeo's placid face with melancholy attention, turned to her husband and placed a hand of nervous deprecation on his arm. He did not look at her.

' Oh, of course, if you don't want to go, if you don't want to go . . ." said the visitor, shaking his head as though at rubbish, and rising several times on his toes. "Perhaps you've a better job," he added, with an unpleasant smile.

"I'm ready to go if you are, sir," said Yeo, "but I shall have to take my friend with me." The sailor nodded my way.

The man did not look at me. I was not there to him. He gave an impatient jerk to his head.

Old Junk

" Ready to go? Of course I'm ready to go! Of course. Why do you suppose I asked? "

Yeo went indoors, came out with a bundle of tarpaulins for us, and began moving with deliberation along to the *Mona*. Something was said by the woman behind us, but so quietly I did not catch it. Her husband made confident noises of amusement, and replied in French that it was always the way with these local folk — always the way. The result, I gathered, of a slow life, though that was hardly the way he put it. Nothing in it, she could be sure. These difficulties were made to raise the price. The morning was beautiful. Still, if she did not want to go . . . if she did not want to go. And his tone was that perhaps she would be as absurd as that. I heard no more, and both followed us.

I got out to the *Mona,* cast off her stern mooring, got in the anchor, and the pull on that brought us to the stone steps of the landing-stage. While I made the seats ready for the voyagers and handed them in, Yeo took two reefs in the lugsail (an act which seemed, I must say, with what wind we felt there, to be carrying his prescience to bold lengths) and hauled the sail to its place. I went forward to lower the centre keel as he came aft with the sheet in his hand. The *Mona* sidled away, stood out, and then reached for the distant sandhills. The village diminished and concentrated under its hill.

When clear of the shelter of the hill, on the lee foot of which the village shelters from the westerly winds, the *Mona* went over suddenly in a gust which put her gunwale in the wash and kept it there. The dipper came adrift and rattled over. Yeo eased her a bit, and his uncanny eyes never shifted from their fixed scrutiny ahead. Our passenger laughed aloud, for his wife had grasped him at the unexpected movement and the noise. "That's nothing," he assured her. "This is fine."

We cleared the shallows and were in the channel where the weight of the incoming tide raced and climbed. The *Mona's* light bows, meeting the tide, danced ecstatically, sending over us showers which caught in the foot of the sail. The weather in the open was bright and hard, and the sun lost a little of its warmth in the wind, which was north of west. The dunes, which had been evanescent through distance in the wind and light, grew material and great. The combers, breaking diagonally along that forsaken beach, had something ominous to say of the bar. Even I knew that, and turned to look ahead. Out there,

across and above the burnished sea, a regular
series of long shadowy walls were forming. They
advanced slowly, grew darker, and grew higher;
then in their parapets appeared arcs of white, and
at once, where those lines of sombre shadows
had been, there were plunging strata of white
clouds. Other dark bands advanced from seaward continuously. There was a tremor and
sound as of the shock and roll of far thunder.

We went about again, steering for the first outward mark of the fairway, the Mullet Buoy.
Only the last house of the village was now looking
at us remotely, a tiny white cube which frequently
sank, on its precarious ledge of earth, beneath
an intervening upheaval of the waters. The sea
was superior now, as we saw the world from our
little boat. The waters moved in from the outer
with the ease of certain conquest, and the foundering shores vanished under each uplifted send
of the ocean. We rounded the buoy. I could
see the tide holding it down aslant with heavy
strands of water, stretched and taut. About we
went again for the lifeboat-house.

There was no doubt of it now. We should be
baling soon. Yeo, with one brown paw on the
sheet and the other on the tiller, had not moved,
nor even, so he looked, blinked the strange, un-

The Voyage of the *Mona*

frowning eyes peering from under the brim of his hat. The *Mona* came on an even keel by the lifeboat-house, shook her wing for a moment as though in delight, and was off again dancing for the Mid Buoy. She was a live, responsive, and happy bird. "Now, Yeo," said the passenger beside the sailor, beaming in proper enjoyment of this quick and radiant experience. "Didn't I tell you so? What's the matter with this?"

There was nothing the matter with that. The sea was blue and white. The frail coast, now far away, was of green and gold. The sky was the assurance of continued good. Our boat was buoyant energy. That bay, when in its uplifted and sparkling mood, with the extent of its liberty and the coloured promise of its romantic adventure, has no hint at all of the startling suddenness of its shadow, that presage of its complex and impersonal malice.

Yeo turned the big features of his impassive face to his passenger, looked at him as he would at a wilful and ill-mannered child, and said, "In five minutes we shall be round the Mid Buoy. Better go back. If you want to go back, say so now. Soon you won't be able to. We may be kept out. If we are, don't blame me."

"Oh, go on, you," the man said, smiling indulgently. He was not going to relinquish the fine gift of this splendid time.

Yeo put his pipe in his mouth and resumed his stare outwards. He said no more. On we went, skimming over inflowing ridges with exhilarating undulations, light as a sandpiper. It was really right to call that a glorious morning. I heard the curlews fluting among the stones of the Morte Bank, which must then have been almost awash; but I did not look that way, for the nearing view of the big seas breaking ahead of us fixed my mind with the first intentness of anxiety. Though near the top of the flood, the fairway could not be made out. What from the distance had appeared orderly ranks of surf had become a convulsive wilderness of foam, piled and dazzling, the incontinent smother of a heavy ground swell; for after all, though the wind needed watching, it was nothing much. The *Mona* danced on towards the anxious place. Except the distant hills there was no shore. Our hills were of water now we neared the bar. They appeared ahead with surprising suddenness, came straight at us as though they had been looking for us, and the discovery made them eager; and then, when the head of the living mass was looking over our boat, it swung under us.

The Voyage of the *Mona*

We were beyond the bar before we knew it.
There were a few minutes when, on either hand
of the *Mona,* but not near enough to be more than
an arresting spectacle, ponderous glassy billows
ceaselessly arose, projected wonderful curves of
translucent parapets which threw shadows ahead
of their deliberate advance, lost their delicate
poise, and became plunging fields of blinding and
hissing snow. We sped past them and were at
sea. Yeo's knowledge of his work gives him
more than the dexterity which overcomes difficulties as it meets them; it gives him the prescience to avoid them.

The steady breeze carried away from us the
noise of that great tumult on the bar, and here
was a sunny quietude where we heard nothing
but the wing of the *Mona* when it fluttered. The
last of the land was the Bar Buoy, weltering and
tolling erratically its melancholy bell in its huge
red cage. That dropped astern. The *Mona,* as
though she had been exuberant with joy at the
promise of release, had come out with whoops and
a fuss, but, being outside, settled down to enjoy
liberty in quiet content. The little lady with us,
for the first time, appeared not sorry to be there.
The boat was dry. The scoured thwarts were
even hot to the touch. Our lady held the brim

[127]

of her big straw hat, looking out over the slow
rhythm of the heavy but unbroken seas, the deep
suspirations of the ocean, and there was even a
smile on her delicate face. She crouched forward
no longer, and did not show that timid hesitation
between her fear of sudden ugly water, when she
would have inclined to her husband's side, and
her evident nervousness also of her mate. She
sat erect, enjoying the slow uplift and descent of
the boat with a responsive body. She gazed over-
side into the transparent deeps, where large jelly-
fish were shining like sunken moons. I got out
my pipe. This suggested something to our other
passenger, and he got out his. He fumbled out
his pouch and filled up. He then regarded the
loaded pipe thoughtfully, but presently put it
away, and leaned forward, gazing at the bottom
of the boat. I caught Yeo's eye in a very solemn
wink.

The *Mona,* lost in the waste, coursed without
apparent purpose. Sometimes for a drowsy
while we headed into the great light shining from
all the Atlantic which stretched before us to America; and again we turned to the coast, which was
low and far beyond mounting seas. By watching
one mark ashore, a grey blur which was really the
tower of a familiar village church, it was clear

The Voyage of the *Mona*

Yeo was not making Pebblecombe with any ease.
I glanced at him, and he shook his head. He then
nodded it towards the western headland of the
bay.

That was almost veiled by a dark curtain,
though not long before the partitioned fields and
colours of its upper slopes were clear as a mosaic;
so insidiously, to the uninitiated, do the moods of
this bay change. Our lady was at this moment
bending solicitously towards her husband, whose
head was in his hands. But he shook her off,
turning away with a face not quite so proud as
it had been, for its complexion had become that of
a green canary's. He had acquired an expression
of holiness, contemplative and sorrowful. The
western coast had disappeared in the murk.
" Better have something to eat now," said Yeo,
" while there's a chance."

The lady, after a hesitating glance at her husband, who made no sign, his face being hidden in
his arms, got out the luncheon-basket. He looked
up once with a face full of misery and reproach,
and said, forgetting the past with boldness,
" Don't you think we'd better be getting back?
It's looking very dark over there."

Yeo munched with calm for a while, swallowed,
and then remarked, while conning the headland,

Old Junk

" It'll be darker yet, and then we shan't go back, because we can't."

The *Mona* continuously soared upwards on the hills and sank again, often trembling now, for the impact of the seas was sharper. The man got into the bottom of the boat and groaned.

Light clouds, the feathery growth of the threatening obscurity which had hidden the western land, first spread to dim the light of the sun, then grew thick and dark overhead too, leaving us, after one ray that sought us out again and at once died, in a chill gloom. The glassy seas at once became opaque and bleak. Their surface was roughened with gusts. The delicate colours of the world, its hopeful spaciousness, its dancing light, the high blue vault, abruptly changed to the dim, cold, restricted outlook of age. We waited.

As Yeo luffed the squall fell on us bodily with a great weight of wind and white rain, pressing us into the sea. The *Mona* made ineffective leaps, trying to get release from her imprisonment, but only succeeded in pouring water over the inert figure lying on the bottom boards. In a spasm of fear he sprang up and began to scramble wildly towards his wife, who in her nervousness was gripping the gunwale, but was facing the affair silently and pluckily. " Keep still there ! " peremptorily ordered the sailor; and the man bundled down without a word, like a dog, an abject heap of wet rags.

The first weight of the squall was released. The *Mona* eased. But the rain set in with steadiness and definition. Nothing was in sight but the waves shaping in the murk and passing us, and the blurred outline of a ketch labouring under reduced canvas to leeward. The bundle on the boat's floor sat up painfully and glanced over the gunwale. He made no attempt to disguise his complete defeat by our circumstances. He saw the ketch, saw she was bigger, and humbly and loudly implored Yeo to put him aboard. He did not look at his wife. His misery was in full possession of him. When near to the ketch we saw something was wrong with a flag she was flying. We got round to her lee quarter and hailed the three muffled figures on her deck.

" Can we come aboard? " roared Yeo.

One of the figures came to the ship's side and leaned over. " All right," we heard, " if you don't mind sailing with a corpse."

Yeo put it to his passengers. The woman said nothing. Her pale face, pitifully tiny and appealing within a sailor's tarpaulin hat, showed an innocent mind startled by the brutality of a world

she did not know, but a mind controlled and alert.
You could guess she expected nothing now but
the worst, and had been schooling herself to face
it. Her husband, when he knew what was on that
ship, repudiated the vessel with horror. Yet we
had no sooner fallen slightly away than he looked
up again, was reminded once more that she stood
so much higher than our boat, and cried, " Yes,
yes ! "

The two craft imperceptibly approached, as by
gravitation. The men of the ketch saw we had
changed our minds, and made ready to receive
us. On one noisy uplift of a wave we got the
lady inboard. Waiting another opportunity,
floundering about below the black wall of the ship,
presently it came, and we shoved over just anyhow the helpless bulk of the man. He disappeared within the ship like a shapeless sack, and
bumped like one. When I got over, I saw the
Mona's mast, which was thrusting and falling by
the side of the ketch, making wild oscillations and
eccentrics, suddenly vanish; and then appeared
Yeo, who carried a tow-line aft and made fast. ·

The skipper of the ketch had been drowned, we
were told. They were bringing his body home.
The helmsman indicated a form lashed in a sail-
cloth to the hatch. They were standing on and

off, waiting to get it over the bar. Yeo they
knew so well that hardly any words passed between them. They were glad to put the piloting
in his hands. He took the wheel of the *Judy of
Padstow.*

The substantial deck of the *Judy* was a great
relief after the dizzy gyrations of the aerial
Mona; and our lady, with a half-glance at what
on the hatch was so grimly indifferent to all that
could happen now, even smiled again, perhaps with
a new sense of safety. She saw her husband settled in a place not too wet, and got about the venerable boards of the *Judy,* looking at the old gear
with curiosity, glancing, with her head dropped
back, into the dark intricacy of rigging upheld by
the ponderous mainmast as it swayed back and
forth. Every time the men went hurriedly tramp-
ling to some point of the running gear she watched
what they were at. For hours we beat about, in a
great noise of waters, waiting for that opportunity
at the entrance to home and comfort. Once Yeo
took us as far towards the vague mist of surf as
the dismal tolling of the Bar Buoy, but evidently
did not like the look of it, and stood out again.

At last, having decided, he shouted orders,
there was a burst of activity, and we headed for
the bad place. Soon we should know.

Old Junk

The *Judy* began to plunge alarmingly. The incoming rollers at times swept her along with a rush, and Yeo had his hands full. Her bowsprit yawned, rose and fell hurriedly, the *Judy's* unsteady dexter pointing in nervous excitement at what was ahead of her. But Yeo held her to it, though those heavy following seas so demoralized the *Judy* that it was clear it was all Yeo could do to keep her to her course. Columns of spray exploded ahead, driving in on us like shot.

"Look out!" cried Yeo. I looked. Astern was a grey hill, high over us, fast overtaking us, the white turmoil of its summit already streaming down its long slope. It accelerated, as if it could see it would soon be too late. It nearly was, but not quite. A cataract roared over the poop, and Yeo vanished. The *Judy*, in a panic, made an attempt at a move which would have been fatal then; but she was checked and her head steadied. I could do nothing but hold the lady firm and grasp a pin in its rail. The flood swept us, brawling round the gear, foundering the hatch. For a moment I thought it was a case, and saw nothing but maniacal water. Then the foam subsided to clear torrents which flung about violently with the ship's movement. The men were in the rigging. Yeo was rigid at the wheel, his eyes on the future.

The Voyage of the *Mona*

I could not see the other passenger till his wife screamed, and then I saw him. Two figures rolled in a flood that was pouring to the canting of the deck, and one of them desperately cletched at the other for aid. But the other was the dead skipper, washed from his place on the hatch.

We were over the bar again, and the deck became level. But it remained the bottom of a shallow well in which floated with indifference the one-time master of the *Judy,* face downwards, and who presently stranded amidships. Our passenger reclined on the vacated hatch, his eyes wide with childish and unspoken terror, and fixed on his wife, whose ministering hands he fumbled for as does a child for his mother's when he wakes at night after a dream of evil.

XII.   The Lascar's Walking-Stick

THE big face of Limehouse Church clock stared through the window at us.   It is rather a senseless face, because it is so full of cracks that you can find any hour in it you do not want, especially when in a hurry.   But nobody with a life that had not wide areas of waste leisure in it would ever visit Hammond now, where he lives in a tenement building, in a room which overlooks the roofs and railway arches of Limehouse.   Just outside his window the tower of the church is rather too large and too close.

Hammond has rooms in the tenement which are above the rest of the street.   He surmounts many layers of dense humanity.   The house is not the usual model dwelling.   Once it knew better days. Once it was the residence of a shipowner, in the days when the London docks were full of clippers, and shipowners husbanded their own ships and liked to live near their work.   The house has a broad and noble staircase, having a carved hand-rail as wide as a span; but much of the old and carved interior woodwork of the house is missing — firewood sometimes runs short there — and the rest is buried under years of paint and dirt.

Hammond never knows how many people share the house with him. " I've tried to find out, but the next day one of 'em has died and two more are born." It is such a hive that most of Hammond's friends gave up visiting him after discovering in what place he had secluded himself; but there he stays with his books and his camera, his pubs and his lightermen, Jews, Chinamen, sailors, and dock-labourers. Occasionally a missionary from the studios of Hempstead or Chelsea goes down to sort out Hammond from his surroundings, and to look him over for damage, when found.

" Did I ever tell you about Jabberjee?" Hammond asked me that afternoon.

No, he hadn't. Some of Hammond's work, which he had been showing me, was scattered over the floor, and he stepped among the litter and came and looked through the window with me. "A funny thing happened to me here," he said, " the other evening. A pal of mine died. The bills which advertise for the recovery of his body — you can see 'em in any pub about here — call him Joseph Cherry, commonly called Ginger. He was a lighterman, you know.

Old Junk

There was a sing-song for the benefit of his wife and kids round at the George and Dragon, and I was going.

"On my way I stopped to look in at my favourite pawnshop. Do you know the country about here? Well, you have to mind your eye. You never know what will turn up. I never knew such a place. Not all of Limehouse gets into the Directory, not by a lot. It is bound on the east by China, on the north by Greenland, on the south by Cape Horn, and on the west by London Bridge.

" The main road near here is the foreshore of London. There's no doubt the sea beats on it — unless you are only a Chelsea chap, with your eyes bunged up with paint. All sorts of things drift along. All sorts of wreckage. It's like finding a cocoanut or a palm bole stranded in a Cornish cove. The stories I hear — one of you writer fellers ought to come and stay here, only I suppose you are too busy writing about things that really matter. You are like the bright youths in the art schools, drawing plaster casts till they don't know life when they see it.

"Well, about this pawnshop. It's a sort of pocket — you know those places on the beach where a lot of flotsam strands — oceanic treasure-

[138]

trove. I suppose the currents, for some reason sailors could explain, eddy round this pawnshop and leave things there. That pawnshop is the luckiest corner along our beach, and I stopped to turn over the sea litter.

"Of course, there was a lot of chronometers, and on top of a pile of 'em was a carved cocoanut. South Sea Islands, I suppose. Full of curious involuted lines — a mist of lines — with a face peering through the mist, if you looked close enough. Rows of cheap watches hung on their chains, and there was a lot of second-hand meerschaum pipes, and a walrus tusk, carved about a little. What took my eye was an old Chinese bowl, because inside it was a little jade idol — a fearful little wretch, with mother-o'-pearl eyes. It would squat in your thoughts like a toad, that idol — eh, where does Jabberjee come in? Well, here he comes.

"I didn't know he was coming at all, you understand. I shouldn't have jumped more if the idol had winked at me.

"There stood Jabberjee. I didn't know that was his name, though. He was christened Jabberjee after the trouble, by a learned Limehouse schoolboy, who wore spectacles. Do I make myself clear?"

[139]

Old Junk

I murmured that I was a little dense, but time might carry out improvements. Hammond was talking on, though, without looking at me. " There the Lascar was. Lots of 'em about here, you know. He was the usual bundle of bones and blue cotton rags, and his gunny bags flapped on his stick legs like banners. He looked as uncertain as a candle-flame in a draught. Perhaps he was sixteen. I dunno. Maybe he was sixty. You can't tell these Johnnies. He had a shaven cranium, ·and his tight scalp might have been slipped over the bony bosses of his head with a shoehorn.

" I don't know what he was saying. He cringed, and said something very quickly; I thought he was speaking of something he had concealed on his person. Smuggled goods, likely. Tobacco.

" Looking over his shoulder, wishing he would go away, I saw a policeman in the dusk at the opposite corner, with his eye on us.

" Then I could see something was concealed under the Lascar's flimsies. He seemed trying to keep it quiet. He kept on talking, and I couldn't make out what he was driving at. I was looking at his clothes, wondering what the deuce he had concealed there. At last something

The Lascar's Walking-Stick

came out of his rags. Talk about making you jump! It really did look like the head of a snake. It was, too, but attached to a walking-stick — sort of handle. A scaly head it was, in some shiny material. Its eyes were like a pair of rubies. They picked up the light somehow, and glittered.

" Now listen. I looked up then into the Lascar's face. I was surprised to find he was taller. Much taller. He put his face forward and down, so that I wanted to step back.

" He had an ugly look. He was smiling; the sweep was smiling, as though he knew he was a lot cleverer than I. Another thing. The place was suddenly quiet, and the houses and shops seemed to have fallen far back. The pavement was wider.

" There was something else, I noticed. The bobby had left the street corner, and was walking our way. The curious thing was, though, the more he walked the farther off he got, as though the road was being stretched under his feet.

" Mind you, I was still awake and critical. You know there is a substratum of your mind which is critical, when you are dreaming, standing looking on outside you, like a spectator.

" Then the stick touched my hand. I shouted. I must have yelled jolly loud, I think. I couldn't

[141]

help it. That horrible thing seemed to wriggle in my fingers.

"It was the shout which brought the crowd. There was the policeman. I can't make out how he got there. 'Now, what's your little game?' he said. That brought the buildings up with a rush, and broke the road into the usual clatter.

"It was all quite simple. There was nothing in it then out of the ordinary. Just a usual Lascar, very frightened, waving a cheap cane with a handle like a snake's head. Then another policeman came up in a hurry, and pushed through the crowd. The crowd was on my side, maudlin and sympathetic. They knew all about it. The coolie had tried to stab me. An eager young lady in an apron asked a boy in front — he had just forced through — what was the matter. He knew all about it.

"'The Indian tried to bite the copper.'

"'Tried to bite him?'

"'Not 'arf he didn't.'

"The Hindoo was now nearly hysterical, and the kiddies were picking up his language fast. 'Now then, old Jabberjee,' said one nipper in spectacles. The crowd was laughing, and surging towards the police. I managed to edge out of it.

The Lascar's Walking-Stick

"'What's the trouble?' I asked a carman.

"'You see that P. and O. Johnny?' he said. 'Well, he knocked down that kid'—indicating the boy in spectacles —'and took tuppence from him.'

"I thought a lot about the whole thing on the way home," said Hammond. "I tell you the yarn for you to explain to the chaps who like to base their beliefs on the sure ground of what they can understand."

XIII.   The Extra Hand

OLD George Galsworthy and I sat on the headland above the estuary, looking into the vacancy which was the Atlantic on an entranced silver evening. The sky was overcast. There was no wind, and no direct sun. The light was refined and diffused through a thin veiling of pearl. Sea and sky were one. As though they were suspended in space we saw a tug, having a barque in tow, far but distinct, in the light of the bay, tiny models of ebony set in a vast brightness. They were poised in the illumination, and seemed to be motionless, but we knew they were moving down on us. " Here she comes," said the seaman, " and a fine evening it is for the end of her last voyage." Shipbreakers had bought that barque. She was coming in to be destroyed.

The stillness of the world, and its lustre in which that fine black shape was centred and was moving to her end, made me feel that headlands, sea, and sky knew what was known to the two watchers on the hill. She was condemned. The

The Extra Hand

ship was central, and the regarding world stood about her in silence. Sombre and stately she came, in the manner of the tragic proud, superior to the compelling fussiness of little men, making no resistance. The spring tide was near full. It had flooded the marsh lands below us, but not with water, for those irregular pools resplendent as mirrors were deeps of light. The hedgerows were strips of the earth's rind remaining above a profound. The light below the lines of black hedges was antipodean. The barque moved in slowly. She did not go past the lighthouse, and past our hill, into the harbour beyond, like a ship about the business of her life. She turned into the shallows below us, and stood towards the foot of the hill.

" She's altered a little," meditated Galsworthy. " They've shortened her sticks, those Norwegians, and painted her their beastly mustard colour and white. She's hogbacked, too. Well, she's old." The old man continued his quiet meditation. He was really talking to himself, I think, and I was listening to his thoughts.

" Look ! " cried Galsworthy, suddenly rising, his hand gripping my shoulder. The tug had cast off and was going about. The ship came right on. There was an interval of time between her

[145]

and the shore which was breathless and prolonged.

"She's aground!" exclaimed the old man to himself, and the hand on my shoulder gripped harder. He stood regarding her for some time. "She's done," he said, and presently released me, sitting down beside me again, still looking at her moodily, smoking his pipe. He was silent for a time. Perhaps he had in his mind that he too had taken the ground. It was sunset, and there she was, and there was he, and no more sparkling morning tides out of port for them any more.

Presently he turned to me. "There's a queer story about her. She carried an extra hand. I'll tell you. It's a queer yarn. She had one man at a muster more than signed for her. At night, you couldn't get into the rigging ahead of that chap. There you'd find him just too much ahead of the first lad who had jumped at the call to be properly seen, you know. You could see him, but you couldn't make him out. So the chap behind him was in no hurry, after the first rush. Well, it made it pretty hard for her old man to round up a crew. He had to find men who didn't know her. Men in Poplar who didn't know her, those days, were scarce. She was a London clipper and she carried a famous flag. Everybody knew her but men who weren't sailors.

The Extra Hand

" Well, the boys said she had a bit of gibbet-post about her somewhere. Ah! maybe. I don't know. Anyway, I say she was a fine clipper. I knew her. She was the pick of the bunch, to my eye. But she was full of trouble. I must say that. When she was launched she killed a man. First she stuck on the ways, and then she went off all unexpected, like a bird. That was always a trick of hers. You never knew her. And when she was tired of headwinds, she'd find a dead calm. That was the kind of ship she was. A skipper would look at her, and swear she was the ship for him. The other chaps didn't understand her, he'd say. A ship like that's sure to be good, he'd tell you. But when he'd got her she'd turn his hair grey. She was that sort.

"One voyage she was six weeks beating to westward round Cape Horn. We had a bad time. I'd never seen such seas. We could do no good there. It was a voyage and a half. She lost the second mate overboard, and she lost gear. So the old man put back to the Plate. And, of course, all her crowd deserted, to a man. They said they wanted to see their homes again before they died. They said there was something wrong about that ship, and they left all their truck aboard, and made themselves scarce. The old man scraped up a new crowd. They came aboard at dusk, one day, and they stared about them. ' Look, sir,' said one of them, ' what's that up there? What's that figgerhead in y'r main to'gal-lan' cross-tree?' I was the mate, you know. I talked to that chap. He learned something about getting the booze out of him before he came aboard. He got a move on.

" We were over four months making 'Frisco that voyage, and she the sailer she was. Why, she's logged thirteen knots. But she could get nothing right, not for long. She was like those fine-looking women men can't live without, and can't live with. She'd break a man's heart. When we got back to Blackwall we heard she was sold to foreigners . . . but there she is now, come home to die. I bet old Yeo don't care much about her troubles, though. He'll break her up, troubles and all, and she's for firewood . . . there you are, my dear, there you are . . . but you should have seen her at Blackwall, in the old days . . . what's the East India Dock Road like, these times? "

The next day, at low water, I stood beneath her, and watched a cascade pouring incessantly from a patched wound in her side, for she had been in collision, and that was why she was condemned. She was careened, like a slain thing, and with the dank rocks and weeds about, and that monotonous pour from her wound, she might have been a venerable sea monster from which the life was draining. Yeo hailed me from above, and up the lively rope ladder I went. She had a Norwegian name, but that was not her name. All Poplar knew her once. There she was born. She was one of ours. That stone arch of John Company, the entrance to the East India Dock, once framed her picture, and her topmasts looked down to the Dock Road, when she was at home. I could believe Galsworthy. She was not so empty as she seemed. She had a freight, and Yeo did not know it. Poplar and the days of the clippers! I knew she was invisibly peopled. Of course she was haunted.

The shipwrecker and I went about her canted decks, groped through dark recesses where it might have been the rats we heard, and peered into the sonorous shades of the empty cargo spaces. In the cabins we puzzled over those relics left by her last crew, which, without their associations, seemed to have no reason in them. There was a mocking silence in the cabins. What sort of men were they who were familiar with these doors? And before the northmen had her,

[149]

and she was English, trim, and flew skysails and
studding-sails, and carried lady passengers, who
were the Poplar boys that laughed and yarned
here? She was more mine than Yeo's. Let him
claim her timber. All the rich freight of her
past was mine. I was the intimate of every ghost
she had.

We sat in a cabin which had been her skipper's.
There was a litter on the floor of old newspapers
and documents, receipts for harbour dues, the captain's copies of bills of lading, store lists, and
some picture-postcards from the old man's family.
A lump of indurated plum-duff, like a geological
specimen, was on the table. There was a slant
of sunshine through a square port window, and
it rested on a decayed suit of oilskins. We sat
silent, the shipbreaker having finished estimating
to me, with enthusiasm, what she had of copper.
He was now waiting for his men to return to
work. They were going to take the masts out of
her. But I was wondering what I could do to lay
that ghost of my old shipping parish which this
craft had conjured in my mind. And as we both
sat there, looking at nothing, we heard, at the
end of the alley-way, a door stealthily latch.

Yeo sprang to his feet at once, staring and listening. He looked at me, surprised and puzzled.

The Extra Hand

" Of all the ——" he began, and stopped. He took his seat again. " Why, of course," he said. " She's settling. That's what it is. She's settling. But my men, the fools, will have it there's some one pottering about this ship."

May 1909.

XIV. The Sou'-Wester

THE trees of the Embankment Gardens were nearly stripped of their leaves, and were tossing widely. Shutting the eyes, you could think you heard the sweep of deep-water seas with strident crests. The greater buildings, like St. Paul's, might have been prom-ontories looming in a driving murk. The low sky was dark and riven, and was falling headlong. But I liked the look of it. Here, plainly, was the end of the halcyon days,— good-bye to the sun,— but I felt, for a reason I could not remember and did not try to recall, pleased and satisfied with this gale and its wrack. The clouds seemed curiously familiar. I had seen them before somewhere; they were reminding me of a lucky but forgotten occasion of the past. Whatever it was, no doubt it was better than anything likely to happen to-day. It was something good in an old world we have lost. But it was something of that old world, like an old book which reads the same to-day; or an old friend surviving, who would help to

[152]

make endurable the years to come. I need not try to remember it. I had got it, whatever it was, and that was all the assurance of its wealth I wanted. Then from the river came a call, deep, prolonged, and melancholy. . . .

So that was it! No wonder the low clouds driving, and the wind in the trees, worked that in my mind. The tide was near full. There was a steamer moving in the Pool. She was outward bound.

Outward bound! I saw again the black buildings of a Welsh coaling port at evening, and a vague steamer (but no liner, that was plain enough, no liner), and two men beside me, who were going out with me in her, watching her. She was little more than a shadow with a port light. She gave a deep, shuddering warning. She was off. We had been for a last run round the town. We were to board her in the outer lock. The wind was whining in the telegraph-wires. It was hazing the pools of rain, which were bright and bleak with the last of a brazen yellow sunset. "Happy days!" said one of us. "Who wouldn't sell that little farm? . . . Now we're in for it. It will be the devil of an old, tough night." (Where this night is that friend? Mine-sweeping? Patrolling? Or is he ——

[153]

Old Junk

But I hope not. He was a good fellow and a sailor.)

We were better off than we knew then, though then we thought it would be hard luck for a dog. Our thoughts turned to the snug indoor places of the lighted town behind us; for in the small hours we should be plunging off Hartland; with the Wolf to come, and the Bay after that; and the glass falling. But youth did know it was young, and that this night, wild and forbidding, and the old *Sirius* rolling away into it, would look fine when seen through tobacco smoke in the years to come.

For the light we saw at sea never fades. It survives our voyaging. It shines into the mind and abides there. We watched the horizon steadfastly for lands we did not know. The sun came up each day to a world that was not the same, no matter how it looked. At night we changed our stars. We heard nothing but the wind and the waves, and the quiet voice of a shipmate yarning with his pipe in his mouth. The elements could interrupt us, but not the world. Not a gull of that was left.

And somehow the beginning of a voyage seemed to be always in westerly weather, at the beginning of winter. The English land to me is a twilight coast with clouds like iron above it poised in a windy light of aquamarine, and a sunset of lucid saffron. Against that western light, bright, bare, and penetrating as the ruthless judgment of impersonal divinity, the polished waves mount, outlined as hard as jet, and move towards us. The ship's prow rises to cut out segments of the west; falls into the dark hollows of waves. The wind pours over us, an icy and ponderable flood, and is increasing. Where England has sunk in the dark one clear eye, like a yellow planet, comes out to watch us.

One thinks of the sea now as something gone, like the old world. There once a voyager was sundered from insistent trifles. He was with simple, elemental things that have been since time began, and he had to meet them with what skill he had, the wind for his friend and adversary, the sun his clock, the stars for counsel, and the varying wilderness his hope and his doubt. But the cruel misery of man did not intrude. He was free from that. All men at sea were his fellows, whatever their language, an ancient fraternity whose bond was a common but unspoken knowledge of a hidden but imminent fate. They could be strangers ashore, but not at sea.

But that is gone now. The sea is poisoned with a deadly sorrow not its own, which man has

put there. The spaciousness of the great vault above the round of waters is soiled by the gibbering anxieties of a thousand gossipers of evil, which the ship catches in its wires, to darken the night of its little company with surmises of distant malignity and woe. It is something to retain a little of the light of the days at sea which have passed. They too had their glooms, but they came of the dignity of advancing storms, and the fear which great seas put in men who held a resolute course nevertheless, knowing that their weird was one which good seamen have faced since first the unknown beyond the land was dared; faith, courage, and the loyalty of comrades, which all the waters of the world cannot drown. But the heart of man, which will face the worst the elements can do, sickens at the thought of the perverse and inexplicable cruelty of his fellows.

October 1917.

XV. On Leave

COMING out of Victoria Station into the
stir of London again, on leave from
Flanders, must give as near the sensation
of being thrust suddenly into life from the beyond and the dead as mortal man may expect to
know.   It is a surprising and providential waken-
ing into a world which long ago went dark.   That
world is strangely loud, bright, and alive.   Plainly
it did not stop when, somehow, it vanished once
upon a time.   There its vivid circulation moves,
and the buses are so usual, the people so brisk
and intent on their own concerns, the signs so
startlingly familiar, that the man who is home
again begins to doubt that he has been absent, that
he has been dead.   But his uniform must surely
mean something, and its stains something more!

And there can be no doubt about it, as you
stand there a trifle dizzy in London once more.
You really have come back from another world;
and you have the curious idea that you may be
invisible in this old world.   In a sense you know

Old Junk

you are unseen.   These people will never know
what you know.   Ther they gossip in the hall,
and leisurely survey the bookstall, and they would
never guess it, but you have just returned from
hell.   What could they say if you told them?
They would be embarrassed, polite, forbearing,
kindly, and smiling, and they would mention the
matter afterwards as a queer adventure with a
poor devil who was evidently a little over-
wrought; shell shock, of course.   Beastly thing,
shell shock.   Seems to affect the nerves.

They would not understand.   They will never
understand.   What is the use of standing in
veritable daylight, and telling the living, who have
never been dead, of the other place?

I know now how Rip Van Winkle felt about it.
But his was a minor trouble.   All he lost was
some years.   He had not changed, except that his
beard was longer.   But the man who comes back
from the line has lost more than years.   He has
lost his original self.   People failed to recognize
Rip because they did not know his beard.   Our
friends do recognize us when they greet us on our
return from the front, but they do not know us
because we are not the men they remember.
They are the same as ever; but when they address
us, they talk to a mind which is not there, though

On Leave

the eyes betray nothing of the difference. They
talk to those who have come back to life to see
them again, but who cannot tell them what has
happened, and dare not try.

Between that old self and the man they see,
there is an abyss of dread. He has passed
through it. To them the war is official *com-
muniqués*, the amplifying dispatches of war correspondents, the silence of absent friends in
danger, the shock of a telegram, and rather interesting food-rationing. They think it is the
same war which the leave-man knows. He will
tell them all about it, and they will learn the truth
at last.

All about it! If an apparition of the battle-
line in eruption were to form over London, over
Paris, over Berlin, a sinister mirage, near, unfad-
ing, and admonitory, with spectral figures moving
in its reflected fires and its gloom, and the echoes
of their cries were heard, and murmurs of convulsive shocks, and the wind over the roofs
brought ghostly and abominable smells into our
streets; and if that were to haunt us by day and
night, a phantom from which there was no escape,
to remain till the sins of Europe were expiated,
we should soon forget politics and arguments, and
be in sackcloth and ashes, positive no longer, but

down on our knees before Heaven in awe at this revelation of social guilt, asking simply what we must do to be saved.

Your revival at home, when on leave, is full of wonderful commonplaces, especially now, with summer ripening. The yellow-hammer is heard on the telegraph wire, and the voices of children in the wood, and the dust of white English country roads is smelled at evening. All that is a delight which is miraculous in its intensity. But it is very lonesome and far. It is curious to feel that you are really there, delighting in the vividness of this recollection of the past, and yet balked by the knowledge that you are, nevertheless, outside this world of home, though it looks and smells and sounds so close; and that you may never enter it again. It is like the landscape in a mirror, the luminous projection of what is behind you. But you are not there. It is recognized, but viewed now apart and aloof, a chance glimpse at the secure and enduring place from which you came, vouchsafed to one who must soon return to the secret darkness in his mind.

The home folk do not know this, and may not be told — I mean they may not be told why it is so. The youngster who is home on leave, though he may not have reasoned it out, knows that what

On Leave

he wants to say, often prompted by indignation, cannot be said. He feels intuitively that this is beyond his power to express. Besides, if he were to begin, where would he end? He cannot trust himself. What would happen if he uncovered, in a sunny and innocent breakfast-room, the horror he knows? If he spoke out? His people would not understand him. They would think he was mad. They would be sorry, dammit. Sorry for him! Why, he is not sorry for himself. He can stand it now he knows what it is like. He can stand it — if they can. And he realizes they can stand it, and are merely anxious about his welfare, the welfare which does not trouble him in the least, for he has looked into the depth of evil, and for him the earth has changed; and he rather despises it. He has seen all he wants to see of it. Let it go, dammit. If they don't mind the change, and don't kick, why should he? What a hell of a world to be born into; and once it did look so jolly good, too! He is shy, cheery, but inexorably silent on what he knows. Some old fool said to him once, " It must be pretty bad out there? " Pretty bad! What a lark!

But for his senior, who also knows, though the feeling is the same, the nature of the combative adult male is less shy, and not merely negatively

Old Junk

contemptuous, but aggressive. It is difficult for him to endure hearing the home folk speak with the confidence of special revelation of the war they have not seen, when he, who has been in it, has contradictory minds about it. They are so assured that they think there can be no other view; and they bear out their mathematical arguments with maps and figures. It might be a chess tournament. He feels at last his anger beginning to smoulder. He feels a bleak and impalpable alienation from those who are all the world to him. He understands at last that they also are in the mirror, projected from his world that was, and that now he cannot come near them. Yet though he knows it, they do not. The greatest evil of war — this is what staggers you when you come home, feeling you know the worst of it — is the unconscious indifference to war's obscene blasphemy against life of the men and women who have the assurance that they will never be called on to experience it. Out there, comrades in a common and unlightened affliction shake a fist humorously at the disregarding stars, and mock them. Let the Fates do their worst. The sooner it is over, the better; and, while waiting, they will take it out of Old Jerry. He is the only one out of whom they can take it. They

On Leave

are to throw away their world and die, so they must take it out of somebody. Therefore Jerry " gets it in the neck." Men under the irrefragable compulsion of a common spell, who are selected for sacrifice in the fervour of a general obsession, but who are cooly awake to the unreason which locks the minds of their fellows, will burst into fury at the bond they feel. The obvious obstruction is the obstinate " blighter " with a machine-gun in front of them. At least, they are free to " strafe " him.

But what is the matter with London? The men on leave, when they meet each other, always ask that question without hope, in the seclusion of their confidence and special knowledge. They feel perversely they would sooner be amid the hated filth and smells of the battle-ground than at home. Out there, though possibly mischance may suddenly extinguish the day for them, they will be with those who understand, with comrades who rarely discuss the war except obliquely and with quiet and bitter jesting. Seeing the world has gone wrong, how much better and easier it is to take the likelihood of extinction with men who have the same mental disgust as your own, and can endure it till they die, but who, while they live in the same torment with you, have the unspoken but certain conviction that Europe is a decadent old beast eating her young with insatiable appetite, than to sit in sunny breakfast-rooms with the newspaper maps and positive arguments of the unsaved!

Autumn 1917.

XVI. The Dunes

THE dunes are in another world. They are two miles across the uncertain and hazardous tide races of the estuary. The folk of the village never go over. The dunes are nothing. They are the horizon. They are only seen in idleness, or when the weather is scanned, or an incoming ship is marked. The dunes are but a pallid phantom of land so delicately golden that it is surprising to find it constant. The faint glow of that dilated shore, quavering just above the sea, the sea intensely blue and positive, might wreathe and vanish at any moment in the pour of wind from the Atlantic, whose endless strength easily bears in and over us vast involuted continents of white cloud. The dunes tremble in the broad flood of wind, light, and sea, diaphanous and fading, always on the limit of vision, the point of disappearing, but are established. They are soundless, immaterial, and far, like a pleasing and personal illusion, a

Old Junk

luminous dream of lasting tranquillity in a better but an unapproachable place, and the thought of crossing to them never suggests anything so obvious as a boat. They look like no coast that could be reached.

It was a perverse tide on a windless day which drifted me over. The green mounds of water were flawless, with shadows of mysteries in their clear deeps. The boat and the tide were murmuring to each other secretly. The boat's thwarts were hot and dry in the sun. The serene immensity of the sky, the warmth and dryness of the boat's timbers, the deep and translucent waters, and the coast so low and indistinct that the silent flashing of the combers there might have been on nothing substantial, were all timeless, and could have been but a thought and a desire; they were like a memorable morning in a Floridan cay miraculously returned. The boat did not move; the shore approached, revealed itself. It was something granted on a lucky day. This country would not be on the map.

I landed on a broad margin of sand which the tide had just left. It was filmed with water. It was a mirror in which the sky was inverted. When a breath of air passed over that polished surface it was as though the earth were a shining

The Dunes

bubble which then nearly burst. To dare that foothold might precipitate the intruder on ancient magic to cloudland floating miles beneath the feet. But I had had the propriety to go barefooted, and had lightened my mind before beginning the voyage. Here I felt I was breaking into what was still only the first day, for man had never measured this place with his countless interruptions of darkness. I don't know whether that mirror had ever been darkened till I put my foot in it. After the news I had heard on the quay that morning before starting out, news just arrived from London, the dunes were an unexpected assurance that the earth has an integrity and purity of its own, a quality which even man cannot irreparably soil; that it maintains a pristine health and bloom invulnerable to the best our heroic and intelligent activities can accomplish, and could easily survive our extinction, and even forget it once supported us.

I found an empty bottle among the dry litter and drift above the tide-mark, sole relic, as far as could be seen there, of man. No message was in the bottle. The black bottle itself was forlornly the message, but it lay there unregarded by the bright immemorial genius of that coast. Yet it settled one doubt. This was not a land which

had never known man. It had merely forgotten
it had known him. He had been there, but
whatever difference he had made was of the same
significance now as the dry bladder-wrack, the
mummied gull near by, and the bleached shells.
The next tide probably would hide the memento
for ever. At the time this did not seem an un-
happy thought, though the relic had been our
last witness, so enduring was the tenuous brightness of the place, the shrine of our particular
star, the visible aura of earth. We rarely
see it. It is something to be reminded it is not
lost; that we cannot, whatever else we can do,
put out a celestial light.

Above the steep beach a dry flat opened out,
reached only by gales and the hi, hest of the spring
tides, a wilderness of fine sand, hot and deep, its
surface studded with the opa' ue blue of round
pebbles and mussel shells. It looked too arid to
support life, but sea-rocket with fleshy emerald
stems and lilac flowers was scattered about.
Nothing moved in the waste but an impulsive
small butterfly, blue as a fragment of sky. The
silence of the desert was that of a dream,
but when listening to the quiet, a murmur which
had been below hearing was imagined. The
dunes were quivering with the intensity of some

The Dunes

latent energy, and it might have been that one heard, or else it was the remembrance held by that strand of a storm which had passed, or it might have been the ardent shafts of the sun. At the landward end of the waste, by the foot of the dunes, was an old beam of a ship, harsh with barnacles, its bolt-holes stopped with dust. A spinous shrub grew to one side of it. A solitary wasp, a slender creature in black and gold, quick and emotional, had made a cabin of one of the holes in the timber. For some reason that fragment of a barque was more eloquent of travel, and the work of seamen gone, than any of the craft moored at the quay I left that morning. I smoked a pipe on that timber — for all I knew, not for the first time — and did not feel at all lonely, nor that voyages for the discovery of fairer times were finished.

Now the dunes were close they appeared surprisingly high, and were formed, not like hills, but like the high Alps. They had the peaks and declivities of mountains. Their colour was of old ivory, and the long marram grass which grew on them sparsely was as fine as green hair. The hollowed slope before me was so pale, spacious, and immaculate that there was an instinctive hesitation about taking it. A dark ghost began

slowly to traverse it with outspread arms, a shade
so distinct on that virgin surface that not till the
gull, whose shadow it was, had gone inland, following its shadow over the high yellow ridge,
did I know that I had not been looking at the
personality. But the surface had been darkened,
and I could overcome my hesitation.

From the ridge, the country of the dunes opened
inland with the enlarged likeness of a lunar landscape surveyed in a telescope. It merely appeared to be near. The sand-hills, with their
acute outlines, and their shadows flung rigidly
from their peaks across the pallor of their slopes,
were the apparition of inviolable seclusion. They
could have been waiting upon an event secret from
our knowledge, larger than the measure of our
experience; so they had still the aspect of a strange
world, not only infinitely remote, but superior with
a greater destiny. They were old, greatly older
than the ancient village across the water. Ships
left the village and went by them to sea gay with
the bunting of a first voyage, with a fair wind,
and on a fine morning; and when such a ship came
back long after as an old plank bearded with sea
moss, to the dunes under which it stranded the
day was still the same, vestal and innocent; for
they were on a voyage of greater length and im-

The Dunes

port. They had buried many ships; but, as time moved to them, all on the same day.

Only when resting on a knoll of one of the slopes, where the shadows of a tuft of marram grass above my head lay as thin black wire on the sand, were the dunes caught in part of their secret. There was no sound. I heard the outer world from which I had come only as the whistle of a curlew. It was far away now. To this place, the news I had heard on the quay that morning would have sounded the same as Waterloo, which was yesterday, or the Armada, which was the same day — wasn't it? — or the day before, or as the whistle of a curlew. Here we were outside time. Then I thought I heard a faint whisper, but when I looked round nothing had altered. The shadows of the grass formed a fixed metallic design on the sand. But I heard the whisper again, and with a side glance caught the dune stealthily on the move.

It was alive. When you were not attentive, some of its grains would start furtively, pour in increasing mobility fanwise, and rest instantly when looked at. This hill was fluid, and circulated. It preserved an outline that was fixed through the years, a known, named, and charted locality, only to those to whom one map would serve a lifetime. But it was really unknown. It was on its way. Like the ships that were passing, it also was passing. It was only taking its own time.

Secluded within the inner ranges were little valleys, where, for a while, the dunes had ceased to travel, and were at leisure. I got into a hollow which had a floor of hoary lichen, with bronze hummocks of moss. In this moment of pause it had assumed a look of what we call antiquity. The valley was not abundant with vegetation, but enamelled and jewelled. A more concentrated, hectic, and volatile essence sent up stalks, blades, and sprays, with that direction and restraint which perfection needs. More than in a likelier and fecund spot, in this valley the ichor showed the ardour and flush of its early vitality. Even now it could shape like this, and give these dyes! Chosen by an earth astringent and tonic, the forms were few and personal. Here you should see to what influences our planet is still subject. The shapes in that valley were more than coloured; they were rare jets of light, emerald, orange, blue, and scarlet. Life burned with an original force, a steady virtue. What is " good news "? It depends on the sort of evidence for which we look.

Just showing in the drift on the seaward side

The Dunes

of the valley were some worked stones and a little
brickwork. When the sandhill paused, it had almost covered a building where man once worshipped. I could find nobody afterwards who remembered the church, or had even heard of it.
Yet the doom of this temple, prolonged in its approach but inevitable, to those to whom the altar
once had seemed as indestructible as hope, must on
a day have struck the men who saw at last their
temple's end was near as a hint, vague but glacial,
of the transience of all their affairs.

But what were their affairs? We should have
to know them before we could regret the dry sand
which buried them. The valley looked very well
as it was. It showed no sign of failure. Over
one of the stones of the forgotten altar was a
casual weed which stood like a sign of success and
continuance. It was as indecipherable as the
stone, but the blue of its flowers, still and deep as
rapture, surprising and satisfying as an unexpected
revelation of good, would have been better worth
reading for a knowledge of the heart from which
could be drawn the temper and intensity of that
faith.

August 1917.

[173]

XVII.   Binding a Spell

YOU may never have addressed a meeting of the public, but you have long cherished a vision of a figure (well known to your private mirror) standing where it overlooks an intent and silent multitude to which it communicates with apt and fluent words those things not seen by mortal eyes, the dream of a world not ours. . . . You know what I mean. (Loud and prolonged applause.)

" I should be glad," wrote one who is still unashamed to call himself my friend, " if you could run down here one evening and address a meeting on your experiences. Just conversationally, you know."

A casual sort of letter. Designedly so. But I could see through it. It was an invitation which did not wish to scare me from accepting it. I smiled with serene amusement at its concluding sentence. Conversationally! Why, that would be merely talking; tongue-work; keeping on and on after one usually, if merciful to a freind, lets

[174]

Binding a Spell

him off. I felt instantly that for once it might be even more pleasant to entertain an audience than to be one of the crowd and bored. And it happened that my experiences really did give me something to say, and were exactly what an audience, in war-time, might be glad to hear. I therefore wrote a brief note of acceptance, as one to whom this sort of thing comes ten times a day; and thought no more about it.

No more, that is to say, till I saw the local paper announced me as a coming event, a treat in store. I was on the list. There were those that evening who, instead of going to a theatre, a concert, or to see Vesta Tilley, would come to hear me. I felt then the first cold underdraught of doubt, the chilling intimation from the bleak unknown, where it is your own affair entirely whether you flourish or perish. What a draught! I got up, shut the door, and looked at the day of the month.

That was all right; yet another fortnight!

But what weakness was this? Anybody, could do it, if they knew as much of my subject as did I. Many men would do it, without a tremor, without shame, if they knew next to nothing about it. Look at old Brown, for example, whose only emotions are evoked by being late for dinner, the price of building materials, the scandalous incapacity of workmen, and the restriction of the liberty of the subject by trade unions! He will sit, everybody knows, while wearing plaid trousers and side-whiskers, on the right hand of a peer, in full view of thousands, at a political meeting, untroubled, bland, conscious of his worth, and will rise at the word, thumbs carelessly thrust into his waistcoat pockets, begin with a jest (the same one), and for an hour make aspirates as uncommon as are bathrooms in his many houses.

He has nothing to say, and could not say it if he had; but he can speak in public. You will observe the inference is obvious. One who is really capable of constructive thought (like you and me); who has a wide range of words to choose from even when running; who is touched, by events, to admiration, to indignation, to alarm, to — to all that sort of thing, he could . . . the plastic audience would be in his skilful hands, there is no doubt. (Hear, hear!)

Time passed. As Mr. A. Ward once pointed out, it is a way time has. The night came, as at last I began to fear it would. My brief notes were in my pocket, for I had resolutely put from me the dishonourable and barren safety of a written lecture. In the train — how cold was the

Binding a Spell

night — I wished I had gone more fully into the matter. Slightly shivering, I tried to recall the dry humour of those carefully prepared opening sentences which shortly would prove to my audience that I had their measure, and was at ease; would prove that my elevation on the platform was not merely through four feet of deal planking, but was a real overlooking. But those delicate sentences had broken somehow. They were shards, and not a glitter of humour was sticking to the fragments.

I felt I would rather again approach one of those towns in France, where it was likely you would run into the Uhlans, than go to that lecture hall. No doubt, too, my friend had explained to them what a clever fellow I was, in order to get some reflected glory out of it. Then it would serve him right; there would be two of us.

The hall was nearly full. What surprises one is to find so many ladies present. A most disquieting fact, entirely unforeseen. They sit in the front rows and wait, evidently in a tranquil, alert, and mirthful mind, for you to begin. I could hear their leisurely converse and occasional subdued laughter (about what?) even where, in a sort of frozen, lucid calm, indifferent to my fate, the mood of all Englishmen in moments of ex-

[177]

Old Junk

treme peril, I was handing my hat and coat to my friend in a room behind the platform. All those people out there were waiting for me.

When we got on the platform the chairman told them something about me, I don't know what, but when I looked up it was to find, like the soul in torment, that a multitude of bodiless eyes had fixed me — eyes intent, curious, passionless.

" I call upon — " said the chairman.

I stood up. The sound of my voice uplifted in that silence was the most startling sound I have ever heard. Shortly after that there came the paralysing discovery that it is a gift to be able to think while hundreds wait patiently to see what the thought is like when it comes. This made my brow hot. There was a boy in an Eton suit, sitting in front with his legs wide apart, who was grinning at me through his spectacles. How he got there I don't know. I think he was the gift of the gods. His smile so annoyed me that I forgot myself, which saved me. I just talked to that boy.

Once there was loud laughter. Why? It is inexplicable. I talked for about an hour. About what? Heaven knows. The chairman kindly let me out through a side entrance.

[178]

XVIII. A Division on the March

WE passed a division on the march the other day. Though the British occupy this country, it is not often one sees them as a multitude. When in the trenches, you are concerned with but a handful of your fellows. But just then an interminable river of steel helmets poured along in regular waves.

It is something to be able to say you have seen a British army moving down the straight leagues of a French road through its guarding avenue of trees. My own brother may have been in that host. . . . Yet I never thought of him. A torrent of sounds swamped and submerged my thoughts — the clangour of chains, the rumbling of wheels, the deep growling of guns; and that most ominous and subduing sound in war, the ceaseless rhythmic tramp of armed men marching without music or song, men who, except the menace of their measured progress, that intimation of destiny and fate irresistible, are but a multitude of expressionless masks that glance at you, and pass.

These men are all dressed alike; they are a tide of men. They all look alike. Their mouths are set. They move together with the common, irresistible, uncritical urge of migratory animals. Their eyes fix you in a single ceaseless interrogation. About what?

There is no knowing. Don't ask me what the men are thinking in Flanders; I don't know, and I have been with them since the beginning. And I don't think any one else does.

But once, as this division was passing, one of those little go-carts on perambulator wheels in which the men, holding drag-ropes, transport their own personal belongings, upset a few books. You would have recognized their popular covers; and the anxiety, instantly shown, to recover those treasures, broke up the formation there for a few moments into something human and understandable. The wind took a few escaped leaves and blew them to me. The *Pickwick Papers!*

It was as though the inscrutable eye of the army had tipped me a wink.

I got the hint that I was, in the right sense, on the same road as these men. My brother was certainly there. For sometimes, you know, one

A Division on the March

has a bleak sense of doubt about that, a feeling
of extreme isolation and polar loneliness. You
wonder, at times, mixed up here in the mysterious
complexities of that elemental impulse which is
visible as ceaseless clouds of fire on the Somme,
whether you are the last man, witnessing in helpless and mute horror the motiveless upheaval of
earth in final ruin.

So that, even as I write this, and glance, safe
for tonight, at the strangeness of this French
house, I see everything about me with astonish-
ment, and feel I may wake at any moment to the
familiar things of that home in which I fell asleep
to dream of calamity.

Moving about this dubious and unauthentic
scene of war, an atom of a fortuitous host, each
one of the host glancing at me with inscrutable
eyes which seem to show in passing — if they
show anything at all — a faint hint of reproach,
the interruption of war by the page of a familiar
book, and the sudden anxious effort by one of the
uniformed phantoms to recover words which you
remember well enough were once worth hearing,
was like momentary recovery. An unexpected
revelation. For a moment I saw the same old
enduring earth under us. All was well.

I often doubt here the existence of a man who

Old Junk

is talking to me. He seems altogether incredible. He might be talking across the Styx; and I am not sure at the moment on which side of that river I stand. Is he on the right side or am I? Which of us has got the place where a daily sun still rises? Yes, it is the living men here who are the uncanny spectres.

I have come in a lonely spot upon a little cross by the wayside, and have been stopped by a familiar name on it. Dead? No. There, right enough, is my veritable friend, as I knew and admired him. He cannot be dead. But those men in muddy clothes who sometimes consort with me round the burning logs on the hearth of an old château at night, I look across the floor at them as across countless ages, and listen to their voices till they sound unintelligibly from a remote and alien past. I do not know what they say to me. I am encompassed by dark and insoluble magic, and have forgotten the Open Sesame, though I try hard to remember it; for these present circumstances and the beings who move in them are of a world unreal and unreasonable.

I get up from the talk of war by that fireside of an old château built on a still more ancient field where English archers fought a famous bottle six hundred years ago. A candle stands on a bracket

A Division on the March

beneath a portrait of a lady. The lady is in the dress of the days of the French Revolution. She is young and vivid, and looks down at me under lowered eyelids in amused and enticing scrutiny. Her little mouth has the faintest trace of a contemplative smile; and as I look at her I could swear the corners of her mouth twitch, as if in the restraint of complete understanding.

She is long gone. She was executed at Arras. But I know her well. The château is less cold and lonely than it was.

Old stairs wind upwards to a long corridor, the distant ends of which are unseen. A few candles gutter in the draughts. The shadows leap. The place is so still that I can hear the antique timbers talking. But something is without which is not the noise of the wind. I listen, and hear it again, the darkness throbbing; the badly adjusted horizon of outer night thudding on the earth — the incessant guns of the great war.

And I come, for this night at least, to my room. On the wall is a tiny silver Christ on a crucifix; and above that the portrait of a child, who fixes me in the surprise of innocence, questioning and loveable, the very look of warm April and timid but confiding light. I sleep with the knowledge of that over me, an assurance greater than that

Old Junk

of all the guns of all the hosts.   It is a promise.
I may wake to the earth I used to know in the
morning.

Winter 1917.

XIX.   Holly-Ho!

IN the train bound for the leave boat, just
before Christmas, the Knight-Errant, who
also was returning to the front, re-wrote the
well-known hymn of Phillips Brooks for me, to
make the time pass.   It began:

> " Oh little town of Bethlehem,
>   To thee we give the lie."

So you may guess, though I shan't tell you, how
it continued.   For the iron was in the soul of the
Knight and misery was twisting it.   I cannot pre-
tend it was a pleasure trip.   This was to be our
third Christmas in Flanders.   Is it any good trying to pass on the emotion common to men who
go to that place because they must?   No, it is
not.   Yet, throughout the journey to the boat,
I was not astonished at the loud gaiety of many
of our passengers.   I have got used to it; for they
were like that when they landed at Boulogne in
August 1914; and they will be no different when

Old Junk

they come back for good, to comfortable observers who prefer to be satisfied easily.

There was a noise of musical instruments and untractable boots on the floor-boards. While waiting in the nervous queue on the Day of Judgment one of those fellows will address a mouth organ to the responsive feet of a pal, and the others will look on with intent approval, indifferent to Gabriel. Having watched disaster experiment variously with my countrymen for three years, I begin to understand why once the French hated us, why lately they have learned to admire us and to be amused by us, why the blunders of our governing classes don't damage us vitally (which seems miraculous unless you know the reason) ; and, indeed, why that blessed flag has braved a thousand years the battle and the breeze.

It is because the quality of our Nobodies (about whom a great epic will get written when a poet is born good enough and big enough to receive the inspiration), it is because any average Nobody has a cool impregnability to the worst bad luck can do which is supernal. That gives the affair something of the comic. That is what makes the humour of the front. And after the first silent pause of respect and wonder at one more story of the sort a journalist knows so well who knows

Holly-Ho!

but a little of railway men and miners, seam-stresses and the mothers in mean streets, and ships and the sea, one cannot help chuckling. Again, the sons of Smith and Jones and Robin! The well-born, the clever, the haughty, and the greedy, in their fear, pride, and wilfulness, and the perplexity of their scheming, make a general mess of the world. Forthwith in a panic they cry, " Calamity cometh! "

Then out from their obscurity, where they dwelt because of their low worth, arise the No-bodies; because theirs is the historic job of re-storing again the upset balance of affairs. They make no fuss about it. Theirs is always the hard and dirty work. They have always done it. If they don't do it, it will not be done. They fall with a will and without complaint upon the wreck-age wilfully made of generations of such labour as theirs, to get the world right again, to make it habitable again, though not for themselves; for them, they must spend the rest of their lives re-creating order out of chaos. A hopeless task; but they continue at it unmurmuring, giving their bodies without stint, as once they gave their labour, to the fields and the sea. And some day the planet will get back to its old place under the sun; but not for them, not for them.

Old Junk

A Nobody never seems to know anything, but by the grace of God he gets there just the same. I was not far from Ypres and the line of the Yser during the first battle for the Channel ports. Do you know how near we were to the edge of the precipice not long before that Christmas? We were on the verge. We were nearly over. I knew it then. So when, later still, I used to meet in France an enigmatic, clay-coloured figure with a visage seamed with humorous dolours, loaded with pioneering and warlike implements, rifles, knives, tin hats, and gas masks, I always felt I ought to get down and walk. Instead of which he used to salute me as smartly as he could. He will never know how cheap and embarrassed he used to make me feel. I wish I knew enough to do him some justice.

And here once more is the leave boat, and this is another Christmas Eve. It was a still twilight, with a calm sea and a swell on our starboard beam. We rolled. We looked back on England sinking in the night. A black smudge of a destroyer followed us over with its eye on us. The main deck was crowded with soldiers — you could not get along there — singing in their lifebelts; at times the chorus, if approved, became a unanimous roar. They didn't want to be there. They didn't want

Holly-Ho!

to die. They wanted to go home. But they sang with dolorous joy. The chorus died; and we heard again the deep monody of the sea, like the admonitory voice of fate. The battles of the Somme were to come before the next Christmas; though none of us on that boat knew it then. And where is the young officer who went ashore under the electric glare of the base port, singing also, and bearing a Christmas tree? Where is that wild lieutenant of the Black Watch — he had a splendid eye, and a voice for a Burns midnight — who cried rollicking answers from the back of the crowd to the peremptory megaphone of the landing officer, till the ship was loud and gay, and the authorities got really wild? And the boy of a new draft, whose face, as I passed him where he had fallen in,— the light dropped to it,— was pale and nervous, and his teeth chattering! Ah, the men we met in France, and the faces we saw briefly, but remember, that were before the Somme! Shadows, shadows.

It rained next morning. This was Christmas Day. We were going to the trenches. Christians awake, salute the happy morn. There was a prospect of straight road with an avenue of diminishing poplars going east, in an inky smear, to the Germans and infinity. The rain lashed

into my northerly ear, and the A.S.C. motor-car
driver, who was mad, kept missing three-ton lor-
ries and gun-limbers by the width of the paint.
One transport mule, who pretended to be frightened of us, but whose father was the devil and
his mother an ass, plunged into a pond of black
Flanders mud as we passed, and raked us with
solvent filth. We wiped it off our mouths. God
rest you merry, gentlemen. A land so inundated
that it inverted the raw and alien sky was on
either hand. The mud clung to the horses and
mules like dangling walnuts and bunches of earthy
and glistening grapes. The men humped themselves in soddened khaki. The noise of the wheels
bearing guns was like the sound of doom. The
rain it rained. O come, all ye faithful!

We got to a place where there was no more
wheeled traffic. There was nothing moving,
nothing alive. That country was apparently
abandoned. To our front and left, for no apparent reason, three little dirty yellow clouds
burst simultaneously over a copse, with a smash
which made you feel you ought to be tolerant to
men with shell-shock. On our right was an empty
field. Short momentary flames leaped constantly
from its farthermost hedge, with a noise like the
rapid slamming of a row of iron doors. Heavy

Holly-Ho!

eruptions, as though subterranean, were going on all the time, the Lord knew where. But not a man was in sight till we got to a village which looked like Gomorrah the day after it happened. Some smoke and red dust were just settling by one of the ruins, and a man lay there motionless with his face in the rubbish. . . .

There was a habitation where sacking kept the wind and rain from unlucky holes, with holly behind pictures tacked to its walls, and a special piece of inviting mistletoe over a saucy lady from *La Vie Parisienne*. There was an elderly and serious colonel, who had an ancestor at Chevy Chase, but himself held independent views on war; and a bunch of modest boys with sparkling eyes and blithe and ironic comments. They also did not discuss the war in the way it is discussed where war is but lowered street lights. We had bully beef, the right sort of pudding,— those boys must have had very nice sisters,— and frosted cake. There were noises without, as the book of the play has it, and plenty of laughter within, and I enjoyed myself with a sort of veiled, subconscious misery; for I liked those lads; and we are so transitory today.

Then one of them took me for a Christmas walk in his country. " Have you got your gas helmet?" he said. "That's right. It makes your eyes stream with tears, and you look such a silly ass." On we went. I began Christmas Day in the trenches by discovering the bottom of the mud too late; though you never can tell, when a noise like the collapse of an iron roof goes off behind you, where you are going to put your feet at that moment. We went through a little wood, where the trees were like broken poles with chewed ends. Over our heads were invisible things which moaned, shrieked, and roared in flight. It was astonishing that they were invisible. Sometimes the bottom of the mud of that communication trench was close, and sometimes not; you knew when you had tried. And as the parapets usually had dissolved at the more dubious places, and I was told and heard that Fritz had machine guns trained on them, I did not waste much time experimenting.

I found the firing-line, as one usually does, with surprise. There was a barrier of sandbags, oozing grey slime, and below, in a sort of little cave, with his body partly resting in a pool of water, a soldier asleep. Just beyond was a figure so merged in the environment of aqueous muck and slime that I did not see him till he moved, and his boots squelched. He lifted a wet rag in the

Holly-Ho!

grey wall and got surprisingly rapid with a rifle which was thrust through the hole and went off; and then turned to look at us. " That fellow opposite is a nuisance," said my officer. " He's always potting at this corner." " Yes, sir," said the figure of mud, darkly louring under its tin hat, " but I know where the blighter is now, and I'll get the beggar yet." With a sudden recollection he then touched iron, and grinned.

Slithering above the ankles in well-worked paste, and leaning against a wall of slime, I tried to find " the nuisance opposite " with a periscope; but before me was only a tangle of rusty wire, a number of raw holes in shabby green grass, some objects lying about which looked like tailors' dummies discarded to the weather, and an awe-inspiring stillness.

There were some interchanges with serious men, who did not sing, but who sat about in mud, or leaned against it, and were covered with it, or who were waiting with rifles ready, or looking through periscopes, or doing things over fires which smoked till the eyes were red. " Come and see our mine crater," said my guide. " It's a topper. Fritz made it, but we've got it."

I knew where that crater would be, and I thought the less of it as a spectacle. But " out

Old Junk

there " one must follow one's leader wherever he goes.   He was going to make me crawl after him in " No Man's Land," and it was not dark yet. So I acquired that sinking sensation described in the pill advertisements.   The mud got down our collars; but we arrived, though I don't know how, because I was thinking too much.   It was only a deep yellow hole in the ground, too, that crater, with barbed wire spilled into it and round it; and you were warned to breathe gently in it, for Fritz might lob a bomb over.   He was six yards off.

In the forlorn and dying light of that Christmas Day I then noticed a muffled youngster beside me, who might have been your son, alone, gripping a rifle with a fixed bayonet, his thoughts Heaven knows where, a box of bombs ready to hand in the filth; and his charge was to give first warning of movement in that stillness beyond. As we crawled away, leaving him there, I turned to look at that boy of yours, and his eyes met mine. . . .

December 1916.

XX. The Ruins

FOR more than two years this town could not have been more remote from us if it had been in another planet. We were but a few miles from it, but the hills hid it, and the enemy was between us and the hills. This town was but a name, a legend.

Now the enemy had left it. When going into it for the first time you had the feeling that either you or the town was bewitched. Were you really there? Were time and space abolished? Or perhaps the town itself was supernatural; it was spectral, projected by unknowable evil. And for what purpose? Suspicious of its silence, of its solitude, of all its aspects, you verified its stones by touching them, and looked about for signs that men had once been there.

Such a town, which has long been in the zone of fire, and is then uncovered by the foe, gives a wayfarer who early ventures into it the feeling that this is the day after the Last Day, and that he has been overlooked. Somehow he did not

Old Junk

hear Gabriel's trumpet; everybody else has gone on. There is not a sound but the subdued crackling of flames hidden somewhere in the overthrown and abandoned. There is no movement but where faint smoke is wreathing slowly across the deserted streets. The unexpected collapse of a wall or cornice is frightful. So is the silence which follows. A starved kitten, which shapes out of nothing and is there complete and instantaneous at your feet — ginger stripes, and a mew which is weak, but a veritable voice of the living — is first a great surprise, and then a ridiculous comfort. It follows you about. When you miss it, you go back to look for it — to find the miserable object racing frantically to meet you. Lonely? The Poles are not more desolate. There is no place as forlorn as that where man once was established and busy, where the patient work of his hands is all round, but where silence has fallen like a secret so dense that you feel that if it were not also so desperately invisible you could grasp a corner of it, lift the dark veil, and learn a little of what was the doom of those who have vanished. What happened to them?

It cannot be guessed. House fronts have collapsed in rubble across the road. There is a smell of opened vaults. All the homes are blind.

The Ruins

Their eyes have been put out. Many of the buildings are without roofs, and their walls have come down to raw serrations. Slates and tiles have avalanched into the street, or the roof itself is entire, but has dropped sideways over the ruin below as a drunken cap over the dissolute. The lower floors are heaps of damp mortar and bricks. Very rarely a solitary picture hangs awry on the wall of a house where there is no other sign that it was ever inhabited. I saw in such a room the portrait of a child who in some moment long ago laughed while it clasped a dog in a garden. You continue to gaze at a sign like that, you don't know why, as though something you cannot name might be divined, if you could but hit upon the key to the spell. What is the name of the evil that has fallen on mankind?

The gardens beyond are to be seen through the thin and gaping walls of the streets, and there, overturned and defaced by shell-bursts and the crude subsoil thrown out from dug-outs, a few ragged shrubs survive. A rustic bower is lumbered with empty bottles, meat tins, a bird-cage, and ugly litter and fragments. It is the flies which find these gardens pleasant. Theirs is now the only voice of Summer, as though they were loathly in the mouth of Summer's carcase. It is perplexing to find how little remains of the common things of the household: a broken doll, a child's boot, a trampled bonnet. Once in such a town I found a corn-chandler's ledger.

It was lying open in the muck of the roadway, wet and discoloured. Till that moment I had not come to the point of believing the place. The town was not humane. It was not credible. It might have been, for all I could tell, a simulacrum of the work of men. Perhaps it was the patient and particular mimicry of us by an unknown power, a power which was alarmingly interested in our doings; and in a frenzy over its partial failure it had attempted to demolish its laborious semblance of what we do. Was this power still observant of its work, and conscious of intruders? All this was a sinister warning of something invisible and malign, which brooded over our affairs, knew us too well, though omitting the heart of us, and it was mocking us now by defiling in an inhuman rage its own caricature of our appearance.

But there, lying in the road, was that corn-chandler's ledger. It was the first understandable thing I had seen that day. I began to believe these abandoned and silent ruins had lived and flourished, had once a warm kindred life mov-

The Ruins

ing in their empty chambers; enclosed a comfort-
albe community, like placid Casterbridge. Men
did stand here on sunny market days, and sorted
wheat in the hollows of their hands. And with
all that wide and hideous disaster of the Somme
around it was suddenly understood (as when an
essential light at home, but a light that has been
casually valued, goes out, and leaves you to the
dark) that an elderly farmer, looking for the
best seed corn in the market-place, while his daugh-
ter the dairymaid is flirting with his neighbour's
son, are more to us than all the Importances and
the Great Ones who in all history till now have
proudly and expertly tended their culture of dis-
cords.

I don't know that I ever read a book with more
interest than that corn-chandler's ledger; though
at one time, when it was merely a commonplace
record of the common life which circulated there,
testifying to its industry and the response of
earth, it would have been no matter to me. Not
for such successes are our flags displayed and our
bells set pealing. It named customers at Thiep-
val, Martinpuich, Courcelette, Combles, Longue-
val, Contalmaison, Pozières, Guillemont, Mon-
tauban. It was not easy to understand it, my
knowledge of those places being what it was.

Old Junk

Those villages did not exist, except as corruption in a land that was tumbled into waves of glistening clay where the bodies of men were rotting disregarded like those of dogs sprawled on a midden. My knowledge of that country, got with some fatigue, anxiety, fright and on certain days dull contempt for the worst that could happen, because it seemed that nothing could matter any more, my idea of that country was such that the contrast of those ledger accounts was uncanny and unbelievable. Yet amid all the misery and horror of the Somme, with its shattering reminder of finality and futility at every step whichever way you turned, that ledger in the road, with none to read it, was the gospel promising that life should rise again; the suggestion of a forgotten but surviving virtue which would return, and cover the dread we knew, till a ploughman of the future would stop at rare relics, holding them up to the sun, and dimly recall ancient tales of woe.

Spring 1917.

XXI. Lent, 1918

IT was Meredith's country, and Atlantic
weather in Lent. The downs were dilated
and clear as though seen through crystal.
A far company of pines on the high skyline were
magnified into delicate inky figures. The vacant
sward below them was as lucent as the slope of a
vast approaching wave. A blackbird was fluting
after a shower, for the sky was transient blue
with the dark rags of the squall flying fast over
the hill towards London. The thatched roof of
a cottage in the valley suddenly flamed with a
light of no earthly fire, as though a god had arrived, and that was the sign. Miss Muffet, whose
profile, having the breeze and the surprise of the
sun in her hair, was dedicated with a quivering
and aureate nimbus, pulled aside the brush of a
small yew, and exclaimed; for there, neatly set
in the angle of the bough, was a brown cup with
three blue eggs in it. I saw all this, and tried
my best to get back to it; but I was not there. I
saw it clearly — the late shower glittered on my

coat and on the yew with the nest in it — but it was a scene remote as a memorable hour of a Surrey April of years ago. I could not approach; so I went back into the house.

But there was no escape. For I freely own that I am one of those who refused to believe there would be " a great offensive." (Curse such trite and sounding words, which put measureless misery through the mind as unconsciously as a boy repeats something of Euclid.) I believe that no man would now dare to order it. The soldiers, I knew, with all the signs before them, still could not credit that it would be done. The futile wickedness of these slaughters had been proved too often. They get nowhere. They settle nothing. This last, if it came, would be worse than all the rest in its magnitude and horror; it would deprive Europe of a multitude more of our diminishing youth, and end, in the exhaustion of its impetus, with peace no nearer than before. The old and indurated Importances in authority, safe far behind the lines, would shrink from squandering humanity's remaining gold of its life, even though their ignoble ends were yet un-achieved. But it had been ordered. Age, its blind jealousy for control now stark mad, impo-tent in all but the will and the power to command

Lent, 1918

and punish, ignoring every obvious lesson of the past, the appeal of the tortured for the sun again and leisure even to weep, and the untimely bones of the young as usual now as flints in the earth of Europe, had deliberately put out the glimmer of dawn.

Well for those who may read the papers without personal knowledge of what happens when such a combat has begun; but to know, and to be useless; to be looking with that knowledge at Meredith's country in radiant April! There are occasions, though luckily they come but once or twice in life, when the mind is shocked by the basal verities apparently moving as though they were fugitive; thought becomes dizzy at the daylight earth suddenly falling away at one's feet to the vacuity of the night. Some choice had to be made. I recalled another such mental convulsion: by Amiens Cathedral, near midnight, nearly four years ago, with the French guns rumbling through the city in retreat, and the certainty that the enemy would be there by morning on his way to Paris. One thing a campaigner learns: that matters are rarely quite so bad or so good as they seem. Saying this to my friend, the farmer (who replied that, in any case, he must go and look to the cows), I turned to some books.

Old Junk

Yet resolution is needed to get the thoughts indoors at such a time. They are out of command.
A fire is necessary. You must sit beside a company of flames leaping from a solidly established
fire, flames curling out of the lambent craters of a
deep centre; and steadily look into that. After
a while your hand goes out slowly for the book.
It has become acceptable. You have got your
thoughts home. They were of no use in France,
dwelling upon those villages and cross-roads you
once knew, now spouting smoke and flames, where
good friends are waiting, having had their last
look on earth, as the doomed rearguards.

The best books for refuge in times of stress are
of the "notebook" and "table-talk" kind.
Poetry I have tried, but could not approach it.
It is too distant. Romance, which many found
good, would never hold my attention. But I had
Samuel Butler's *Note Books* with me for two
years in France, and found that the right sort of
thing. You may begin anywhere. There are no
threads to look for. And you may stop for a
time, while some strange notion of the author's is
in contest for the command of the intelligence with
your dark, resurgent thoughts; but Butler always
won. His mental activity is too fibrous, masculine,
and unexpected for any nonsense. But I had to

Lent, 1918

keep a sharp eye on Butler. His singular merits were discovered by others who had no more than heard of him, but found he was exactly what they wanted. If his volume of *Note Books* is not the best example of its sort we have, then I should be glad to learn the name of the best. This Lent I tried Coleridge again. But surely one's mind must be curiously at random to go to such wool-gathering. I found him what I fear Lamb and his friends knew him to be — a tireless and heavy preacher through the murk of whose nebulous scholarship and philosophy the revealing gleams of wisdom are so rare that you are almost too weary to open the eyes to them when they flash. Selden is better, but abstract, legal, and dry.

Hazlitt compelled a renewal of an old respect; his humanity, his instinct for essentials, his cool detection of pretence and cant, however finely disguised, and his English with its frank love for the embodying noun and the active verb, make reading very like the clear, hard, bright, vigorous weather of the downs when the wind is up-Channel. It is bracing. But I discovered another notebook, of which I have heard so little that it shows what good things may be lost in war; for this book was published in 1914. It is the *Impressions and Comments* of Havelock Ellis.

Old Junk

There have been in the past critics of life and the things men do who have been observers as acute, as well-equipped in knowledge, and have had a command of English as free and accurate, as the author of " Impressions and Comments "; but not many. Yet such judgments of men, their affairs and their circumstances, could have been written in no other time than the years just before the war — the first note is dated July, 1912. The reflections are often chill and exposed; but so is a faithful mirror bleak, though polished and gleaming, when held up to grey affairs in the light of a day which is ominous. You seem to feel in this book the cold draught moving before the storm which has not come — the author knew of no storm to come, and does not even hint at it; but the portents, and the look of the minds of his fellows, make him feel uncomfortable, and he asks what ails us. Now we know. It is strange that a book so wise and enlivening, whether it is picturing the Cornish coast in spring, the weakness of peace propaganda, Bianca Stella, Rabelais, the Rules of Art, the Bayeux Tapestry, or Spanish cathedrals, should have been mislaid and forgotten. . . .

The fire is dying. It is grey, fallen, and cold. The house is late and silent. There is no sound

but the ghostly creaking of a stair; our thoughts
are stealing away again. We creep out after
them to the outer gate. What are books and
opinions? The creakings of an old house uneasy
with the heavy remembrances and the melancholy
of antiquity, and with some midnight presage of
its finality.

The wind and rain have passed. There is now
but the icy stillness and quiet of outer space. The
earth is Limbo, the penumbra of a dark and partial recollection; the shadow, vague and dawnless,
over a vast stage from which the consequential
pageant has gone, and is almost forgotten, the
memory of many events merged now into formless
night itself, and foundered profoundly beneath
the glacial brilliance of a clear heaven alive with
stars. Only the stars live, and only the stars over-
look the place that was ours. The war — was
there a war? It must have been long ago. Perhaps the shades are troubled with vestiges of an
old and dreadful sin. If once there were men who
heard certain words and became spellbound, and in
the impulse of that madness forgot that their earth
was good, but very brief, and turned from their
children and women and the cherished work of
their hands to slay each other and destroy their
communities, it all happened just as the leaves of

Old Junk

an autumn that is gone once fell before the sudden
mania of a wind, and are resolved. What year
was that? The leaves of an autumn that is long
past are beyond time. The night is their place,
and only the unknowing stars look down to the
little blot of midnight which was us, and our
pride, and our wisdom, and our heroics.

April 1918.

THE END